THE CONCISE HISTORIES OF **DEVON**

ROMAN
DEVON

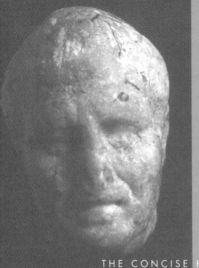

THE CONCISE HISTORIES OF **DEVON**

ROMAN DEVON

MALCOLM TODD

First published in Great Britain by The Mint Press, 2001

ISBN 1-903356-10-5

Cataloguing in Publication Data
CIP record for this title is available from the British Library

The Mint Press
18 The Mint
Exeter, Devon
England EX4 3BL

Cover and text design by Delphine Jones

Main cover illustration, marble portrait bust, mid to late first century AD, found at Goldsmith Street, Exeter (Exeter City Museums) photograph courtesy of Exeter Archaeology Unit
Coin: gold aureus of AD 75-9 found in Exeter (courtesy Exeter City Museums)

Printed and bound in Great Britain
by Short Run Press Ltd, Exeter.

CONTENTS

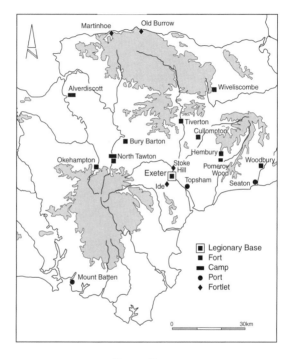

Roman Devon

INVASION
AND
OCCUPATION

I n AD 43 the Roman emperor Claudius
launched an invasion of Britain from
bases in northern Gaul with the intention
of conquering the island, twice invaded,
but not subdued, by Julius Caesar a
century earlier. Within five years much of
southern Britain was in the control of
Roman forces, led by four legions. In AD
49, a Roman city (colonia) was established

at *Camulodunum* (Colchester), thus indelibly stamping Roman authority on this addition to the Empire. Other Roman settlements quickly emerged, at London, Canterbury, Silchester, Chichester and elsewhere, in some cases with the aid or connivance of British leaders, some of whom had earlier established contacts with the Roman superpower in western Europe. The tribes of southern Britain were not able, or willing, to mount serious resistance to the Roman advance in the early campaigns. By AD 47, the south and much of the east was secured for Rome. By AD 49, the mineral deposits of the Mendip hills in Somerset were being worked by Rome. The south-western peninsula was now within Roman grasp. Roman forces were poised to take possession of the territory of the tribe occupying Devon and Cornwall, and by AD 50 this takeover had begun.

It must be stressed that what we know of the Roman invasion and occupation of Devon rests almost entirely on the evidence of archaeology, won by painstaking work on and below ground. No literary or historical sources exist to help us in reconstructing either the broad picture or adding the vital details. The conquest of this remote area of the ancient world was of little interest to the public which Roman writers addressed. But the archaeological record is not negligible and it continues to grow and illuminate the way in which the Dumnonii and their territory were implanted in the greatest empire of the ancient world.

The initial Roman movement into the region might have been expected to be represented by temporary or marching camps, briefly occupied as formations first ranged over a little known territory. But only two such temporary works are so far known in Devon. This is in line with the early situation in Wessex, but contrasts sharply with the later assaults on the Welsh borderland and the Pennines. A temporary camp is known at Alverdiscott in north Devon, but nothing has yet appeared in the east of the county. A key site in the conquest of the region lies at North Tawton, where a complex of military works has been recorded over the past half-century. Traces of two temporary camps are known here, relics of early operations north of Dartmoor. These then seem to have been succeeded by a large fort or campaign base, into one corner of which a small fort was later inserted. A still later work, enclosing 2.7 hectares (6.5 acres) which appears to be a fort and an attached annexe, lies to the south close to the Taw crossing. This is probably the latest fort here. In the annexe there existed a stone structure, possibly a small bath-house. As yet, North Tawton is the only military site in Devon (or the South West) to which Roman forces returned on several occasions, underlining its central importance in the period of conquest.

The earliest Roman military site yet known in Devon is that within the great hill-fort of Hembury near Honiton. The Iron Age fort had been abandoned at least a century before the Roman invasion. A Roman unit arrived here about AD 50, established well-founded timber buildings, reconstructed the two main gates and possibly refurbished the old ramparts. This redoubt was not well suited to control a wide swathe of territory and may have been chosen for its proximity to iron deposits in the Blackdown Hills. Hembury was occupied for no more than twenty years and then dismantled.

The main strike-force in the region, a legion, took up station in a fortress at *Isca* (Exeter), probably between AD 50 and 55. The entire regiment, probably the Second Legion Augusta, may not have been based at Exeter at all times. The silver and lead deposits in Somerset will have been under the control of legionaries, following normal Roman practice at this date and other detachments may have been outstationed in winter-quarters or in campaign-bases in the campaigning season. A likely temporary base for a unit on campaign lay at North Tawton on a major route running north of Dartmoor, a site to which the army returned on several later occasions. To the west a fort at Okehampton carried this route towards the Tamar valley in the vicinity of Launceston.

Essential to the control of recently annexed territory was the security of the major routes and attention was given to this elementary fact from the outset. The main Roman route ways in Devon were similar to those in use today and are clearly related to local geography. Running north from Exeter a route followed the Exe valley, on which lay a fort at Bolham, near Tiverton. Another line followed the valleys of the Taw and Yeo, overseen by a fort at Bury Barton, near Lapford. This route presumably ran through to the lower Taw, ending near Barnstaple, though no evidence has yet been obtained. A third route ran from the Tone valley in Somerset into the Culm valley and thus to Exeter, on a line now followed by the main railway line and the M5 motorway. A fort near Cullompton lay on this line and another may be predicted in Taunton Deane, perhaps at Taunton itself. There are still gaps in the known network of forts and routes. North Devon has produced few sites related to the early Roman occupation. A possible fort lay at Rainsbury on the eastern side of Exmoor. Otherwise, Roman control is represented by two signal fortlets on the coast at Martinhoe and Old Burrow. These cannot have existed in isolation and their garrisons must have been provided from an as yet unlocated fort in the area. These fortlets have been linked with a watch on the Silures of South Wales, but this is unlikely. More plausibly, they were linked with Roman shipping operating in the Bristol Channel.

Another area which has so far produced little evidence of Roman military activity is south and west Devon; more sites must still lie undetected. The deeply indented coastline between the estuaries of the Exe and Tamar offered several excellent harbours which could have facilitated cross-Channel connections and military supply along the coast. The pre-Roman port at Mount Batten on Plymouth Sound no doubt continued in use. A site at Topsham, five km. south of Exeter, was certainly occupied in the mid-first century and may have been an entrepôt for the supply of Exeter.

Roman documents add at least one name for an early Roman base in west Devon. This was *Tamara* or *Tamarus*, clearly a site on the Tamar. Its precise location is not certain but is likely to have been either at the head of the Tamar estuary or at a river–crossing near Launceston. Another much discussed site named in Roman sources is *Moridunum*, 15 Roman miles east of Exeter on the route leading to Dorchester. *Moridunum* should thus lie in the Otter valley, perhaps near Fenny Bridges, near where a small fort has recently been identified at

Pomeroy Wood. Yet another site mentioned in Roman sources bore the name *Derventio statio*, most probably situated in the South Hams, possibly on the lower Dart. This may have originated in a military post of the first century AD. A puzzling site at Woodbury near Axminster may have played a role in the military occupation, in the period between AD 55 and 75. These small posts at Pomeroy Wood, Woodbury and one of the forts at North Tawton represent a phase of consolidation after initial conquest as it became clear that the peninsula was securely held. Some forts, including Tiverton, may have been held into the

70s, to aid policing and tax-collection, but when the legion was withdrawn about AD 74 military occupation gave way to routine administrative duties.

Roman control of the Dumnonii was complete by AD 60. There were no setbacks to Roman rule like that of the rebellion under Boudicca in East Anglia and no prolonged resistance like that encountered in Wales. The incorporation of the Dumnonii into the Roman Empire proceeded without major disruption over the next twenty years.

THE LEGIONARY
FORTRESS
AT
ISCA

T he date at which the legionary base at Exeter was founded has been much discussed and a variety of dates has been proposed. The earliest, AD 50-55, is supported here, though a date of AD 55-60 is possible. Anything later than AD 60, however, is not supported by the evidence at present available. Like other military bases of the first century AD, the Exeter fortress possessed mainly earthwork and timber defences and timber internal buildings. One major building, the baths, was necessarily built in stone and brick (below, p.26). The defensive circuit is now fairly well known. An earth rampart revetted by a timber palisade accompanied by a wide ditch defined an area of about 40 acres (just over 15 hectares). Timber gates no doubt existed at the centre of each side and watch-towers at intervals of about 30 metres stood on the rampart. The fortress occupied a fairly flat area below Rougemont, extending down the slope towards the Exe to either side of the present Fore Street. To the west, the defences ran above the Longbrook valley. A small annexe was attached to the south-west defences and at least two enclosed compounds lay outside the south-east side. A timber aqueduct tapped a spring in the St Sidwells area and led water through the defences near the north gate. Major roads will have led to all the gates, though only those from the north (Sidwell Street) and the east (Topsham Road) are known for certain. The Exe was presumably crossed by a bridge or pontoon, but no details of a structure have been identified.

Within the fortress some 5,000 men were accommodated, mainly legionary infantry but possibly including a small contingent of cavalry. Also present were soldiers' servants and slaves for menial duties. At this date legionaries were full Roman citizens, most of them drawn from the Roman communities of Italy, Spain and Gaul. The commanding officer, the *legatus legionis*, is unknown but will have been of high social rank, a member of the Senate and a man with years of military service behind him and the possibility of high office in a provincial command, or even in Rome itself still to come. The commander of the Second Legion Augusta in the invasion army of AD 43, Vespasian (T. Flavius Vespasianus) was to become emperor after the civil wars of AD 68-9, though this was due to extreme and exceptional circumstances.

A legion was organised in sixty centuries of 80 men, each under the command of a centurion. The centuries were grouped in ten cohorts commanded by tribunes, mainly young officers early in their careers. The first cohort was double the strength of the others and often contained the legionary cavalry. The planning of a legionary base naturally reflected this internal organisation of the unit. At the centre of the fortress, along the main streets lay the headquarters (*principia*), the commander's residence *(praetorium)* and the houses of the tribunes. Behind these lay granaries, workshops and, sometimes, a hospital. Most of the rest of the interior was taken up with barrack accommodation for the centuries, normally about 60, though this varied. The quarters for centurions lay at the end of each barrack block, normally close to the defences. Cooking ovens lay to the rear of the rampart; soldiers ate in their barrack rooms or in the open, tended by their servants.

A legion usually built a substantial stone bath-house, either inside or outside its base. At *Isca* the bath-house was located behind the central range of buildings, in the area now occupied by the Cathedral Yard. This was an imposing structure, built largely of stone from Rougemont, brick and tile. Not all of the building has been excavated. The hot room (*caldarium*), part of the warm room (*tepidarium*) and the main furnaces have been studied, but the cold room (*frigidarium*) and the exercise-hall (*palaestra*) remain unexamined. Although smaller than many legionary baths, the building had been richly furnished with decorative details, including one of the earliest mosaics yet known in Roman Britain, Purbeck marble mouldings and fired clay antefixes placed on the eaves.

This interesting building was well excavated, published and then carefully buried again in case it might one day be exposed once more.

Legionaries included builders and other craftsmen in their ranks. North of the fortress lay a legionary tile-workshop and other trades may well have been practised here, by civilians as well as troops. A Roman garrison of 5,000 well-paid men was a great attraction to civilian traders offering a wide range of commodities and services, as in garrison posts to the present day. Some of these civilian followers probably remained in Exeter after the legion was withdrawn and formed part of the commercial nucleus of the developing city.

The approaches to the fortress were covered on the west side of the Exe valley by a watch-tower above Ide. A site on Stoke Hill, 3 km. north of Exeter, resembles a watch-tower, but excavation has produced little in the way of reliable dating evidence.

Military occupation at *Isca* continued until after AD 70. By that time the pacification of the South-west was complete and Roman attention turned to the final conquest of Wales and the invasion of northern Britain. The precise date at which the Exeter fortress was evacuated cannot be fixed but it was effected by AD 74 as in that year a new base for the Second Legion Augusta was being constructed at Caerleon in South Wales. The fact that the same mould for clay antefixes was used at both Exeter and Caerleon indicates a close link between the two bases, but the full picture may be more complicated than the direct transfer of the Second Legion from Exeter to Caerleon.

At least part of a legion was also in station at Gloucester in the late 60s and early 70s and this unit may have been drawn in whole or in part from Exeter. Whether or not this was the case, Exeter ceased to house a legion after AD 74 at the latest and the following years saw a transition to a different kind of Roman authority.

The Early Roman City

The essential element of Roman administration in the provinces was the creation of urban centres where these did not already exist. In south-western Britain such centres did not exist. In such circumstances, military bases usually provided the nuclei for early urban development and this was the case at Exeter where no substantial pre-Roman settlement existed. A Roman city of any kind was in essence a territory with an urban centre. Virtually all cities in the Roman world depended heavily on their hinterlands and what they could produce; this was certainly true of *Isca* and not only in its early history.

The transition from legionary fortress to early city was not immediate; it may have extended over twenty or more years, though Roman control was not relaxed. Elsewhere in the western Roman provinces, interim arrangements included the appointment of local officials who would supervise the collection of taxes and other dues, keep order and provide the core of an urban community.

Physically, the changes within the old fortress may have been minor in the first ten years. The legionary timber buildings were largely demolished following usual Roman practice, probably with recovery of much usable material. The defensive circuit, however, was retained and survived for the next seventy years, though in an attenuated form. The old ditch slowly silted up and was used as a dump for rubbish. There was obviously no need for substantial protection of the developing city. The legionary bath-house continued in use until about AD 85 and was then largely demolished to make way for the forum and basilica of the city, though parts were incorporated in the new buildings. Private houses in this early phase are not well known at present but they appear to have been timber structures of simple plan. The urban population of the early cities in Roman Britain was small, a few thousand at most. The main system of streets was retained from the military base and a number of new streets added after AD 100. Not all of the new developments lay within the defended circuit. North of the defences in the St Sidwell's area, industrial and craft activities continued to grow and the area close to the bank of the Exe also showed signs of an enlarging economic life.

Pottery production was a major concern outside the northern defences and one potter, or workshop-master, provides us with the first and only named individual in early Roman *Isca*, one Vitanius. The general prosperity resulting from the Roman peace in southern Britain touched Devon and *Isca* without lighting a great economic fire.

At the heart of the new city lay the legal, commercial and administrative headquarters of the community, the forum and basilica. From here the tribal territory, the *civitas* of the Dumnonii was governed, justice dispensed and a varied commerce organised. This building complex was an extensive stone structure, though an earlier timber basilica may have existed for a time. The stone building was completed about AD 90 or shortly afterwards. In this same area there will have been sited a major temple to the ancestral gods of Rome. South-west of the forum lay an open area which may have served as an animal market. A new public bath-house was built about AD 100 in the area of the later Deanery close to South Street. The main public buildings were thus in place early in the second century. At that stage the city was enclosed but poorly protected by the old legionary defences. By the middle of the second century those defences had become ruinous and were virtually out of use. Early *Isca* was to all intents an open city.

Urban Change, Isca from the Second Century to the Fourth

The Roman city underwent considerable change in the next two centuries. By about AD 175, new urban defences were provided in the form of an earthen rampart, possibly faced by a simple timber revetment, and two large external ditches. The area enclosed, measuring 37 hectares (89 acres), was an irregular polygon. On the western side, the city defences followed those of the legionary fortress for half of the side above the Longbrook valley. Elsewhere, they followed a new course, surrounding much more space than had previously been built over. These defences did not long continue without modification. In the early third century, a substantial wall of Rougemont stone was added to the front of the rampart and stone gates replaced whatever had earlier existed at the entry points. Although the stone gates have long disappeared, long stretches of the city wall can still be seen behind Southernhay, in Northernhay gardens and below South Street. Within the city the third century saw major changes. A few new streets were built in the recently enclosed areas, while some of the older streets went out of use and were later built over. More profound was the change registered in urban housing. As the third century proceeded several large houses emerged in replacement of a more egalitarian system of housing. Several of these dwellings had ancillary buildings and small enclosures in their vicinity and were probably the centres of agricultural and craft activities. This phenomenon is known elsewhere in late Roman Britain, for example at Cirencester and Silchester. The social change these houses imply were thus probably a general development. The forum complex was partially rebuilt or repaired in the later fourth century and could have continued to stand until well into the fifth century. Sizeable areas were open in the late Roman period, as in many other cities in southern Britain. Deposits of black earth built up in the third and fourth centuries, though their precise significance is not clear.

Although the urban community may have reduced in size in this phase, the identity of the Dumnonii had not been destroyed. Two inscriptions record building or repair on Hadrian's Wall by the *civitas Dumnoniorum* in either the third or early fourth century.

SETTLEMENT
ON THE
LAND

People do not live in a vacuum and in antiquity almost the entire population were close to the land and the natural environment. We cannot yet reconstruct the natural world of early Devon in detail but the information we now possess is beginning to provide a basis for a fuller understanding of environmental change over a lengthy period. Although Devon is now a largely pastoral region, there is good evidence for cereal cultivation on some scale, particularly of wheat and barley. The Roman fort at Bury Barton has produced substantial quantities of carbonised wheat and cereal pollen. In lowland Devon the pollen record indicates the presence of wheat and oats in a relatively open landscape. Although arable farming was practised in these areas, extensive grassland was also present. In the valleys, the trees included many species familiar today: oak, alder, beech, willow, birch and elm.

The great majority of the population of Devon under Roman rule continued to live in the kinds of settlement that had predominated in the Iron Age. Large nucleated settlements are virtually unknown. The major hill-forts had been abandoned before the Roman conquest, although some still held a limited population in the first century AD. Unlike the peoples to the east of the Dumnonii, no major centre of political and economic power is known within the tribal area. A large enclosed site at Wind Hill, Countisbury in north Devon may have been a central place within its landscape but nothing is known of its cultural context. The largely rural population was scattered across the land in small homesteads and single farms. Many of these were enclosed by a bank or bank and ditch or ditches. They were varied in form. Rectilinear enclosures bounded by either or two ditches are very widely represented in south Devon in particular, though are found elsewhere. Unfortunately very few have been excavated or even sampled as yet. The few that have been examined have not been informative as to their social context and economic basis. The generally acid soils of the region are not helpful to the preservation of vegetation remains, except in wet conditions, and animal bones are even rarer survivors. The internal buildings of these enclosed sites are also little known and many may always be difficult to identify by excavation. Although there is a fair presumption that some of these sites were first occupied in the later prehistoric period, present evidence suggests that many were Romano-British in date. The scarcity of later Iron Age pottery is a major inhibition in establishing a reliable cultural sequence and chronology. The present Romano-British emphasis may thus be misleading.

One site with at least a degree of continuity from a pre-Roman community is that at Milber Down, near Coffinswell,

Newton Abbot. Here a hill-slope fort surrounded by three substantial ramparts was occupied down to the early first century AD. At or shortly after the abandonment of the fort, a group of three small bronze figurines, a bird, a duck and a stag, were concealed in the middle ditch, possibly recording a symbolic act at the close of occupation. Either shortly afterwards or possibly immediately, a small rectangular enclosure was added to the earlier work on its up-slope side. This was occupied within the first century AD, c. AD 50 to 80. A group of small fields or closes lay close by, no doubt supporting agricultural activity, which may have continued after the enclosure was abandoned. Timber buildings existed within the site but their plan is uncertain. One of the incidental, and very welcome, results of the Milber Down sites is the evidence for the contemporary vegetation. Iron Age and Roman deposits produced evidence for oak, hazel, plum, cherry, hawthorn and gorse, to which might be added ash and poplar.

More recent examination of a rectilinear enclosure has been carried out at Hayes Farm, close to the A30 at Clyst Honiton. This formed only one element in a complex landscape which also included at least two ring-ditches of prehistoric date and at least two other enclosures. Only parts of two enclosures have been examined, so any conclusions must be provisional. One sharp-angled enclosure was evidently occupied from at least the second century AD onward, possibly down to the fourth, though earlier activity is not excluded.

No coherent remains of buildings were found within the enclosing bank and ditch, though evidence of timber structures could have been destroyed by ploughing. On the other hand, an area barely 20 metres square was available to accommodate structures: perhaps the main nucleus of settlement lay elsewhere.

Occupation in the early post-Roman period has been suggested for a later phase, but this rests insecurely on a single radio-carbon date. One of the most interesting results from Hayes Farm is the evidence for cultivated crops and other vegetation in the Roman period. The main cereal crops represented were spelt and emmer wheat, notably spelt, barley and possibly oats, though the last-named may not have been a cultivated plant. Seeds of grasses were probably derived from pasture areas in the vicinity of arable fields.

Not all the Romano-British rural settlements have produced a record of impoverishment in their material culture. A small, almost square enclosure at Stoke Gabriel, set within embanked fields, had received plain samian ware from central Gaul in the early second century and, half a century earlier a bronze brooch of a type widely distributed in southern Britain. Much less usual are fragments of three Roman glass vessels, two bottles and a bowl. The position of Stoke Gabriel close to the estuary of the Dart probably gave it access to wider markets serviced by coastal trade. Occupation does not seem to have been continuous within the known enclosure. A gap may have occurred in the middle Roman centuries, but occupation was certainly maintained in the fourth century, as eight Roman coins reveal. These, too, are far from usual finds on rural settlements in the region.

One of the most completely excavated enclosures is that at Rudge, near Morchard Bishop. This lay on a terraced hill-slope and was first revealed on the ground by the appearance of two ditches in parched grassland. An inner ditch largely enclosed a space of less than half an acre, within which lay one or possibly two timber round houses. The site as a whole was only briefly occupied, between AD 55 and 80, the same period in which the nearby fort of Bury Barton was held. Given the very modest nature of the Rudge enclosure and its buildings, the material from the site, especially the pottery, is of surprisingly high quality, including Roman table wares and flagons, and even fragments of a wine amphora. These must be related to the presence of the Roman garrison at Bury Barton 2 km. away. How the occupants acquired this material and the food and drink it implies can only be guessed at but most probably they were able, and more than willing, to supply goods and services to the relatively affluent troops stationed across the Yeo valley.

In central Devon, between Dartmoor and Exmoor, there existed a religious centre which had probably survived from the pre-Roman Iron Age into Roman Britain. No single site has been identified, but a number of place- names contain the Celtic element *nemeton*, meaning "sacred grove". The surviving names (e.g. Nymet Rowland, Broad Nymet, Nymetwood, Kings Nympton, Nymet Tracy among others) point to the middle valley of the Taw as the likely location of the nemeton. Its survival into the Roman period is demonstrated by the record of a site named *Nemetostatio* in this area in a late Roman document. The best candidate for this site is the enclosed site at Bury Barton, known to have been occupied in the late Roman period.

It might have been expected that occupation would have been resumed in some of the hill-forts of Devon in the late and post-Roman period, though there is little sign of this at present, unlike the situation in Somerset. Even the prominent forts in east Devon, such as Hembury, Sidbury and Dumpdon have so far given up no indication that they housed communities in this period. It must be stressed, however, that few sites have been examined on any scale and the scarcity of any material after about AD 400 presents serious problems to the identification of any kind of settlement site. It seems unlikely that these sites were wholly ignored in the fluid conditions of early post-Roman Devon. Two hill-forts have produced a little evidence to suggest occupation at the end of the Roman period. Cadbury, between Crediton and Tiverton, contained a shaft 18 metres deep into which personal ornaments (bracelets, rings and beads) had been thrown late in the fourth century or later. This was obviously a votive deposit, of a kind well known in southern Britain. Another shaft may have lain within the hill-fort of Dolbury above Killerton in east Devon.

This is poorly recorded, but the geological formation of the hill makes it unlikely that this was a well. The shaft is filled and has never been archaeologically examined.

It can be expected that the landed elite of the Dumnonii exploited the good land which the region offered, especially in the east and the south. A small number of villas are known and the discovery of others is a reasonable prediction. One of the recently identified sites is a villa southeast of Crediton, recorded from the air in some detail. This was a substantial house of six or seven rooms, fronted by wings linked by a portico. This evidently prosperous farm was set in a ditched enclosure or, just possibly, had developed from an enclosed farmstead, as at the Holcombe villa (below). Three other sites in east Devon may have been Romanised farms. At Thorverton in the Exe valley, finds of Roman building material are suggestive of a substantial building. Overlooking the Exe estuary at Exmouth building material and a scatter of Roman coins may represent a villa site or possibly port buildings. Another site, at Otterton Point close to the coast, is yet another candidate for a villa, though the site is incompletely known.

The most interesting of the known villas, and the best known, is the house at

Holcombe, Uplyme, close to the Dorset border. This had grown from modest origins in the late Iron Age and early Roman period into a substantial, but by no means luxurious, dwelling in the fourth century. But one architectural feature gives it distinction, an octagonal structure added at one end of the house after AD 300. This is usually interpreted as a bath-house, centred on an octagonal plunge or pool, but there are problems with this identification. The disposition of rooms in the building does not conform to those of the usual Roman baths. Also, there was very limited provision for the supply of water and for the drainage away of waste. This striking building is better seen as a pavilion with a central pool, which might be used for lustral purposes, perhaps even Christian baptism. A strikingly similar building existed at a villa at Lufton in Somerset, again more reminiscent of a baptistery than a bath-house. When we recall that several villas in southern Britain, including two in Dorset (Hinton St Mary and Frampton), have produced convincing evidence for early Christian families, the idea receives at least general support.

Although at least three major roads can still be traced in the region, numerous minor routes no doubt existed, but were not metalled and are thus difficult to detect. The Fosse Way approached from the north-east and may have entered the extreme east of the county to a terminus at Seaton. It was crossed by a road running west from Dorchester in Dorset to Exeter, passing broadly from Axminster to Honiton and turning sharply in the Otter valley. West of Exeter, a road climbed over Haldon and ran on to the Teign near Newton Abbot, possibly crossing the river by a timber bridge of which large piles have been recovered from the bed. North of Dartmoor, a prominent road line can be traced in lanes and hedgebanks between Yeoford and North Tawton and this presumably ran east to Exeter, perhaps via the Creedy valley.

A site at Woodbury near Axminster on the Roman road from Dorchester to Exeter, succeeding a small military post, may have served as an official road-station (*mansio*) or may have developed as a minor township on the main road, like so many others in southern Britain. Limited excavation and prospection here suggests the existence of stone buildings of the second to fourth centuries. Much more intensive work is needed to determine the significance of the site. Its siting on the main east-west route is of obvious interest but what is known at present gives no sign of any official status. It is also interesting that nothing resembling the Woodbury site has been identified west of Exeter. It is at least possible that Woodbury lay on the border of the canton of the Durotriges to the east and the Dumnonii to the west, but without further work speculation can go no further.

Few individual objects reached the shores of Devon from the wider Roman world. A small marble head of a man (featured on the cover) found at Exeter is an import, though precisely when it arrived in the city is unknown. A piece of sculpture with an impeccable pedigree is the torso of a large bird in Purbeck marble, dating to the late first century. This is possibly the earliest sculptured piece in Purbeck marble yet known in Britain. Fragmentary as it is this is a fine figure, which may have originally belonged to a larger figured ensemble, possibly a victory monument. Sculpture in stone is otherwise rare and no native tradition seems to have emerged. Objects in other media are equally scarce. The most striking is a bronze mount, probably from a couch or other fine piece of furniture. It was cast in the form of a centaur being ridden by a young boy, perhaps Achilles, in pursuit of a wild animal. Found on the beach at Sidmouth, this fine piece of craftsmanship may have come from a wreck. In origin, there is no doubt that it came from the Mediterranean world or from Gaul.

ECONOMIC
LIFE

As in virtually all areas of the Roman Empire, economic life was based on agriculture and the products which stemmed from it. But the South West of Britain offered another dimension: mineral wealth.

Minerals

Devon offered important mineral resources, something always attractive to

Rome. The tin deposits of Dartmoor were as important, probably more important, than Cornish tin in the Roman period. Tin was of limited use on its own but was versatile in producing alloys, especially bronze and pewter. Later exploitation of the Dartmoor deposits makes it difficult to assess the character and extent of Roman extraction of the mineral, but the rise of pewter in the production of table vessels in the later Roman period gave added stimulus to the mining of tin. The South West offered a variety of other minerals, including silver and copper in west Devon and iron in the Blackdown Hills and on Exmoor. Small quantities of gold may also have been available from south Devon rivers and from the area around Crediton.

Little of this mineral wealth will have benefitted the inhabitants of the region. Most of the mineral products left the area and the profits creamed off by entrepreneurs based elsewhere. In the later Roman period, after AD 300, the growth of a command economy increasingly concentrated natural resources in official hands.

The natural deposits of tin on Dartmoor lay close to the surface or were exposed in the moorland valleys. Extraction of the mineral was probably mainly, or wholly, by the process of "streaming" in which stream deposits were excavated from the surface and the fragments of tin ore (cassiterite) washed out or collected. The results of the streaming process can still be seen in many areas of Dartmoor, especially in the centre and the south, but it is as yet impossible to distinguish the work of Romano-British streamers from that of later workers operating in much the same way. A few Roman objects, including coins and pottery, have been reported from the stream-workings, but these are not securely stratified and give no clear guidance on precise dating and no more on who was doing the work and disposing of the metal.

As most of the tin will have been transported out of the South West, finds of tin ingots in the region are far from common. By far the single most important find is a group of 44 ingots from a wreck on the sea-bed in Bigbury Bay. Most of these were in the shape of a flattish bun, though a few were shaped like knuckle-bones *(astragaloi)*, as noted by the Greek writer Diodorus. Bigbury Bay lies close to the tin deposits of the Erme and the Avon and may thus have been a significant centre of export along the coast and perhaps across to Gaul. Unfortunately, the Bigbury ingots are not closely dated, but they seem more likely to belong to the

Roman or early mediaeval period than to any later phase. A late Iron Age date is not excluded. More work on the ground will reveal more about this important industry though it will always be difficult to disentangle Iron Age, Roman, mediaeval and later phases of extraction.

Devon also possessed considerable deposits of iron and this metal, too, may have been exported from the region. Iron deposits contributed to the late Iron Age economy, as is suggested by hoards of iron currency bars at Holne Chase and Milber Down in south Devon. The Blackdown Hills were a major source of iron, worked by the Roman army in the first century AD and quite possibly by the late Iron Age population. There were also significant reserves of iron ore on Exmoor and some of these may have been worked in antiquity. Roman coins have been found at iron-working sites just over the border in Somerset and a large complex at Sherracombe Ford has produced radiocarbon dates indicating working and smelting in the late Iron Age and early Roman period.

Pottery

The production of pottery was one of the fundamental industries of any Roman province, serving major sites and modest households alike. The widespread products of the industry are also of vital importance to archaeological study for its contribution to the dating of sites. The military occupiers of the region in the first-century were served by manufactures in western Europe and south-eastern Britain. But local sources of pottery were in operation by AD 60-70. A distinctive utilitarian ware was reaching the legionary fortress at this time, possibly from close at hand. It was supplemented by a black burnished ware produced in the Axe valley, which was distributed to several of the first-century military bases, and by another black burnished ware from south

Dorset. Amphorae containing wine and oil arrived from Spain and from Rhodes.

After the departure of the legion, other local wares began to reach the sites in south Devon. A distinctive strain of pottery was produced in the area of the lower Dart and Erme, most of it wheel-made, but with hand~made large storage vessels. This was widely distributed in Devon and, by coastal trade, in Cornwall and further afield. Beginning in the late first century, this industry provided a high proportion of the pottery used on sites from the second century to the fourth. The pottery of north Devon is not yet well known, for the lack of any major centre. It is likely that it will have been influenced by the strong ceramic traditions of Somerset and Gloucestershire. The south of Devon remained in contact with the Roman West, receiving wine amphorae from north Africa and fine wares (*Céramique a l'éponge*) from the region of Bordeaux. The local industries failed in the late fourth century and faded out altogether shortly after AD 400. Metal vessels may have helped to fill the gap, though most domestic purposes will have been served by containers of wood and leather.

Coinage

A particular phenomenon of the archaeology of south Devon is the presence of Greek coins of silver and bronze on a wide variety of sites. A substantial number was recorded in Exeter in the earlier nineteenth century, some of these fairly certainly modern imports. But not all can be so summarily dismissed. Another series of Greek coins has been recorded in south Dorset and others have appeared around Torbay and on south Dartmoor, in circumstances which often exclude the possibility of recent importation. It is an important fact that a high proportion of these coins were issued by Greek port cities in southern Italy and Sicily; these issues circulated widely in the western Mediterranean.

Some will have entered Britain in the Roman period, but others are more likely to be imports of the late Iron Age, perhaps linked with the trade in metals. Greek coins are now appearing in other Iron Age contexts along the southern coast of Britain, giving further support to the idea of connections between the South West and the western Mediterranean world.

Livestock

The main source of information on the animal population of Devon in the Roman period is animal bones. Unfortunately, the generally acidic soils of Devon have destroyed much of this evidence, except in selected instances. Some sites have produced no bone at all, others only limited samples. The major exception is Exeter where large samples of animal bones have been recovered from most phases of occupation, thus providing an extensive picture of the domestic animals reared and consumed in and around the fortress and the city. Extrapolation to the wider hinterland is dangerous, but the Exeter evidence is the best we presently have for south Devon at least. In the phase of military occupation and its aftermath, the main mass of bone derived from cattle, sheep and goat (these are difficult to distinguish), and pig. Among these, cattle were dominant, as is the case at other military sites in the first century AD. Probably most of the animals were reared for meat, though the hides and the fleeces of sheep were also likely to have been exploited. Wild animals were represented by a surprisingly small number of bones, mainly deer and hare. Horses, too, were only occasionally represented.

As the city developed, the character of the animal population altered somewhat, probably as agricultural exploitation developed in the surrounding area. Sheep/goat and pig increased in proportion, though still fell well short of cattle. Horses and wild animals continued to be minor components of the total population. The overall picture was therefore not substantially changed and it seems to have been maintained throughout the second and third centuries. The limited evidence gathered from rural sites is broadly in line with what has been recorded from Exeter.

The situation somewhat changed in the fourth century. Cattle again formed the dominant element with sheep/goat and pig far behind on the sites examined. Animals were being butchered within the town and at least some may have been permanently housed in certain areas. This change was probably related to a steady alteration in the social and economic fabric of the city in the late Roman period. Now, a small number of larger houses provided new focal points of wealth and economic activity. Unfortunately, it is not possible to deduce from the bones what secondary products such as milk, cheese, hides and glue were derived from the animals, but it is a reasonable assumption that these resources were tapped. A surprising fact is the scarcity of evidence for hunting the abundant game of the area. Fish provided some contribution to diet. Ten different species are represented, including salmon, bass, turbot, wrasse, sea bream, gurnard, hake, cod, whiting and conger eel. These could have been caught by inshore fishing, though some species might have been taken in the estuaries.

ENDING AND
BEGINNING

The latest phases of Roman administration in Devon are poorly recorded but are not redolent of sudden, destructive change. The picture is one of slow decay from the late fourth century onward, presumably against a background of the breakdown of central power. There is no reason to see the region as beset by external enemies at this stage. Very little changed at the end of Roman rule for the majority of the population. In the short term, there may have been benefits, as the burden of Imperial taxation was removed. Roman coinage was reaching Exeter in small and decreasing quantity after c.AD 360 and twenty years later had almost stopped altogether. This is earlier than cities to the east and suggests the elimination of currency for everyday transactions well before the end of Roman administration. The local industries also came to an end by the early fifth century. Pottery and metalwork almost disappear from the scene, making the identification of sites extremely difficult. The virtual absence of locally produced pottery is the most serious single drawback to study of the period after AD 400.

The fifth and sixth centuries, however, are not a total blank, though reading the evidence requires different skills from those demanded by the study of the South West under Rome. There was no evident pressure on the south-western communities by intruders from the east or from the sea. The essentially dispersed settlement of Devon does not lend itself to precise examination, not least as the archaeological standby of pottery and metal artifacts is so limited. A community at Exeter, within secure town walls, no doubt continued, even though firm evidence is very thin. Major structures are unlikely to have been maintained in anything resembling their original form. Parts of the forum complex were partially rebuilt and may have continued in use into the early fifth century at least.

Formally, Britain had been part of a Christian Empire since AD 330. It is not easy to assess what this actually meant in an area like Devon in the fourth and fifth centuries. Direct evidence for a Christian community in any part of the region is lacking. A Chi-Rho monogram scratched on a sherd of pottery found in South Street, Exeter, is of interest, but it does not provide wholly convincing proof of a Christian group in the city. Of greater weight is the presence of an inhumation cemetery in the area of the Cathedral Close. Radiocarbon dates suggest that some of the graves date to the late fifth century. The mere fact that burials were now being sited at the centre of the Roman city not only indicates a radically altered community and its attitude to treatment of its dead. It also suggests the existence of a new focus at the heart of *Isca*. It is not known whether or not this was a church, but this is not out of the question. As the relevant area is largely covered by late Saxon structures and the mediaeval cathedral, opportunities for examination are very limited.

Part of the heritage of Roman Britain in western Britain is an important series of inscribed stones, most of them recording leading individuals, and Devon has produced several of these. As a high proportion of the inscriptions include the formula *hic iacit*, or *hic jacet*, or the word *memoria*, the stones presumably originally marked graves, or were funerary monuments, though many have since been moved to new sites or reused in walls and buildings. Often, no more than the name of the person commemorated is recorded, sometimes with the patronymic, as in the case of Cavudus, son of Civilis, at Lynton. But in a few instances a title might be given, as at Sourton Down near Okehampton a man is described as *Princeps* (chief?) and at Buckland Monachorum, where Dobunnus is mentioned as a *Faber* (smith or metalworker). These inscriptions as a class have long been interpreted as Christian memorials introduced after the end of Roman Britain, probably from the late fifth century onward. There is, in fact, very little evidence for their date and some of the earliest may date from the latest phase of the province or shortly afterwards. At all events, the Latinity and letter-forms of many of the inscriptions indicate strong links with the late Roman world, including northern Gaul as well as Britain.

That the south-western peninsula was not isolated from the wider late Roman world is further demonstrated by finds of imported pottery vessels at several sites, including at least three in Devon. The most significant concentration has been found at Bantham on the Avon estuary, where the coastal dunes have revealed a series of deposits containing pottery from the eastern Mediterranean and North Africa, at the end of long trade routes which took in Spain and western Gaul. The material includes amphorae which once contained wine and oil, and fine table wares with red slip coating. Smaller quantities of imported material has come from Mothecombe on the Erme estuary. In the case of both sites there must have been a return, most probably minerals from the Dartmoor massif.

Another site on the south coast, though in a very different situation, which received imports in the late fifth and sixth centuries is High Peak near Sidmouth. A roughly oval enclosure, now largely destroyed by erosion, occupied a prominent hill-top high above the beach. The imports were mainly amphorae from the eastern Mediterranean, though fine red-slip table ware was found here in the nineteenth century.

Rome's legacy to later Devon cannot be claimed to have been very great. The choice of the site of Exeter at an early stage was formative, but aside from providing a secure defended centre for the post-Roman urban and ecclesiastical community, it is difficult to discern significant threads of continuity between antiquity and the mediaeval centuries. It might be argued that at least the site of the Saxon minster and the Norman cathedral had their origins in the fifth or sixth century, but this is not yet proven.

There may be one relic from the Roman past, one which is easily overlooked: the name of Devon itself. The earliest reference to the early mediaeval population of Devon occurs in the Anglo-Saxon Chronicle in an entry under the year 823. This mentions the Defnas, the people of Devon. There are later references to Defnum and Defenum. All three names are plausibly descended from the name of the Dumnonii. In other respects, Devon's participation in the Roman Empire lay buried in the past.

FURTHER READING

Much of the primary evidence for Devon in antiquity is presented in the Proceedings of the Devon Archaeological Society and its predecessor the Proceedings of the Devon Archaeological Exploration Society. Important general works include A. Fox, *South-West England* (London, 1964; 2nd ed Newton Abbot, 1973), M. Todd, *The South-West to AD 1000* (London, 1987), F. M. Griffith, *Devon's Past: an Aerial View* (Exeter, 1988), R. Kain & W. Ravenhill (ed.), *Historical Atlas of South-West England* (Exeter, 1999) and S. Pearce, *The Kingdom of Dumnonia* (Padstow, 1978). Major excavation reports and related studies are: A. Fox, *Roman Exeter: Excavations in the War-damaged Areas 1945-7* (Manchester, 1952), J. Collis, *Exeter Excavations: the*

Guildhall Site (Exeter, 1972), P. Bidwell, *The Legionary Bath-house and Forum and Basilica at Exeter* (Exeter, 1979), M. Maltby, *The Animal Bones from Exeter, 1971-5* (Sheffield, 1979), B. Cunliffe, *The Iron Age and Roman Port at Mount Batten, Plymouth* (Oxford, 1988) and N. Holbrook & P. Bidwell, *Roman Finds from Exeter* (Exeter, 1991).

There are many general works on Roman Britain. Among the most useful are S.S. Frere, *Britannia* (3rd ed. London, 1987), M. Millett, *Roman Britain* (London, 1995) and J. Wacher, *The Towns of Roman Britain* (2nd ed. London 1995).

Gold Roman aureus depicting the Empeoror Vespasian, AD 75-79
(courtesy Exeter Museums Service)

Also available in the Concise Histories of Devon Series

The Vikings and Devon	Derek Gore
Elizabethan Devon	Todd Gray
Devon and the Civil War	Mark Stoyle

Also by **The Mint Press**

The Devon Engraved Series

Exeter Engraved: The Secular City (2000)

Exeter Engraved: The Cathedral, Churches, Chapels and Priories (2001)

Devon Country Houses and Gardens Engraved (2001)

Dartmoor Engraved (2001)

The Travellers' Tales Series

Exeter (2000)

East Devon (2000)

Cornwall (2000)

The Bush Theatre presents
the world premiere of

Falling

by Shelley Silas

Directed by John Tiffany
Designed by Martin Reynolds
Lighting Design by Tanya Burns
Sound Design by Scott George for Aura Sound Design Ltd.

12 – 30 November 2002

Cast

Kate	Jennifer Black
Grace	Abby Ford
Linda	Patricia Kerrigan
Pete	Adam Kotz

Director	John Tiffany
Designer	Martin Reynolds
Lighting Designer	Tanya Burns
Sound Designer	Scott George for Aura Sound Design Ltd
Deputy Stage Manager	Nasarene Asghar

Press Representation	The Sarah Mitchell Partnership 020 7434 1944
Marketing Consultation	Sam McAuley for Chamberlain McAuley 020 8858 5545
Advertising and Graphic Design	M & H Communications 020 7412 2000

The Bush Theatre would like to offer special thanks to Annabelle Apsion, Ian Curtis, Louisa Milwood-Haigh, Celia Robertson and all those individuals and companies who have generously given in-kind support to this production and the Naked Talent Season.

This performance lasts approximately 2 hours 15 minutes including a 15-minute interval

This play received its world premiere at The Bush Theatre on 14 November 2002

King's Men, Dangerfield, Casualty, Driving Ambition, The Mushroom Picker, Whistleblower (all BBC), *Spooks* (Kudos/BBC), *Mr White Goes To Westminster* (Hat Trick), *Midsomer Murders* (Bentley Productions), *Secret Passage* (Delux Productions), *Without A Clue* (ITC), *Love Potion No 9* (Flying High), *Touching Evil* (United), *Never Never* (Company TV), *Perfect* (Carlton).

Shelley Silas – Writer

Shelley Silas's past works: for Radio 4 – *Calcutta Kosher* (August 2000), *The Magpie Stories* (devised and co-wrote – Feb 2002) and *The Sound of Silence* (June 2002). For theatre: *Calcutta Kosher*, rehearsed reading (Tara Arts, 1998), *Shrapnel*, a short play produced by Steam Industry (BAC, 1999). In 1996 she was a winner in the ICA's New Blood fiction competition with her short story, 'Via Calcutta'. Current projects include *The Wedding Dress* – a 90-minute film for Touchpaper Television, and a new stage play, *Moses Mohammed*. Shelley is currently the Pearson Writer-in-Residence at The Bush Theatre.

John Tiffany – Director

Trained: Glasgow University and on the Regional Theatre Young Directors Scheme at the Traverse Theatre. Associate Director at Paines Plough since October 2001. Literary Director at the Traverse from June 1997 to October 2001. For Paines Plough he directed *Helmet* by Douglas Maxwell (co-production with Traverse Theatre). Other work includes *Gagarin Way* by Gregory Burke (also RNT), *Among Unbroken Hearts* by Henry Adam (also Bush), *Abandonment* by Kate Atkinson, *King Of The Fields* by Stuart Paterson, *The Juju Girl* by Aileen Ritchie, *Danny 306 + Me (4 Ever)* by David Greig (also Birmingham Rep), *Perfect Days* by Liz Lochhead (also Hampstead, Vaudeville and tour), *Greta* by James Duthie and *Passing Places* by Stephen Greenhorn (also Citizens' and tour) for the Traverse. Film includes: *Karmic Mothers* (BBC Tartan Shorts) and *Golden Wedding* (BBC Two Lives).

Martin Reynolds – Designer

Martin studied architecture at the Bartlett School of Architecture, UCL. Martin has a design practice in the East End of London, which combines projects with research, collaborations and teaching. Current projects include a residential house in Dalston and an exhibition at the Imperial War Museum in Manchester. Collaborations include a kinetic installation for performance artist Graeme Miller and a photographic exploration into domesticity with artist Mary Lemley. Previous collaborations range from a sound-scape in Salisbury with Graeme Miller to a building proposal for London's South Bank with artist Richard Wilson and Architects McCormick Jamieson Pritchard. Martin teaches design in London.

Tanya Burns – Lighting Designer

Tanya was awarded the prestigious Arts Foundation Fellowship for Lighting Designers in 1996, and has since gained her MSc in Light and Lighting at UCL's Bartlett School of Architecture. In addition to theatre, she is now a lighting consultant on exhibition, architectural and environmental projects. Most recent work includes; Nasdaq TV Studios, Times Square New York, Coca Cola at Madison Square Gardens, New York, Samsung Pavilion and Exhibition at the Winter Olympics, Salt Lake City (International Gold Award Winner). West End credits include: *Hay Fever* (Savoy); *You'll Have Had Your Hole* (Astoria); *Funny Money* (Playhouse); *The Killing of Sister George* (Ambassadors) and *September Tide* (Comedy). Also in London: *Blackbird* (The Bush); *Been So Long and Cockroach Who?* (Royal Court); *Mules* (Royal Court and Clean Break); *Red and Another Nine Months* (Clean Break); *Ballad of Wolves* (Gate); *All For Love* and *Solitude of the Cotton Fields* (Almeida) and *Saltwater Moon and Miss Julie* (Kings Head). Other work includes: *When We Were Married* (Leicester Haymarket); *Present Laughter* (Birmingham Rep); *Singing In The Rain and Macbeth*, (West Yorkshire Playhouse); *Crimes and Crimes, Mensch Meier, Artificial Jungle, Playboy of the Western World, One Small Step, 42nd Street, Hedda Gabler, East, The Thirst, Thru the Leaves, Decadence and The Caretaker* (Leicester Haymarket); *Dead Meat* (West Yorkshire Playhouse); *Candida* (Plymouth Theatre Royal); *School For Scandal* (RSC, Stratford and Barbican) and *Fantastic Voyage* (Edinburgh Festival) and *Soundbites* (Almeida and ENO Opera Festival). Dance includes *Headshot* (V-Tol Dance Company, The Place and tour).

Scott George – Sound Designer

Scott began working in sound in Australia, and has since brought his skills to almost every continent in the world. Recent design credits in England include: *Sive* (Druid Theatre, Galway), *Cabaret* (Chichester Festival Theatre); *Kosher Harry* (Royal Court); *Maria Friedman In Concert* (West End); The Taming of the Shrew (Nottingham Playhouse), *Bali, Death Of A Salesman, Dolly West's Kitchen, Peter Pan* (Haymarket Theatre, Leicester); *A Buyer's Market, A Carpet, A Pony & A Monkey* (co-design with John Leonard at The Bush); *Journey to the West* (Tara Arts); *The Lost Musicals* (Royal Opera House); *Much Ado About Nothing* (London International Festival at The Guildhall); *The Three Musketeers* (Young Vic). Production Engineering credits include: *Benefactors* (Tour / West End); *The Distance From Here* (Almeida), *Macbeth* (Ludlow Festival); *Saturday Night Fever* (British Tour); *Lulu, Coriolanus/Richard II* (Almeida at Gainsborough Studios, also New York and Tokyo); *Macbeth* (RSC tour); *Plenty* (Almeida at The Albery). In July 2000, Scott became Show-Control Director of Aura Sound Design Ltd.

30 Years of The Bush Theatre

The Bush Theatre opened in April 1972 in the upstairs dining room of The Bush Hotel, Shepherds Bush Green. The room had previously served as Lionel Blair's dance studio. Since then, The Bush has become the country's leading new writing venue with over 350 productions, premiering the finest new writing talent.

Playwrights whose works have been performed here at The Bush include

Stephen Poliakoff, Robert Holman, Tina Brown, Snoo Wilson, John Byrne, Ron Hutchinson, Terry Johnson, Beth Henley, Kevin Elyot, Doug Lucie, Dusty Hughes, Sharman Macdonald, Billy Roche, Tony Kushner, Catherine Johnson, Philip Ridley, Richard Cameron, Jonathan Harvey, Richard Zajdlic, Naomi Wallace, David Eldridge, Conor McPherson, Joe Penhall, Helen Blakeman, Lucy Gannon, Mark O'Rowe and Charlotte Jones.

The theatre has also attracted major acting and directing talents including Bob Hoskins, Alan Rickman, Antony Sher, Stephen Rea, Frances Barber, Lindsay Duncan, Brian Cox, Kate Beckinsale, Patricia Hodge, Simon Callow, Alison Steadman, Jim Broadbent, Tim Roth, Jane Horrocks, Gwen Taylor, Mike Leigh, Mike Figgis, Mike Newell and Richard Wilson.

Victoria Wood and Julie Walters first worked together at The Bush, and Victoria wrote her first sketch on an old typewriter she found backstage.

In 30 years, The Bush has won over one hundred awards. Bush plays have transferred to the West End and Broadway, and have been successfully adapted for film and television. Bush productions have toured throughout Britain, Europe and North America.

Every year we receive over fifteen hundred scripts through the post, and we read them all. According to The Sunday Times:

'What happens at The Bush today is at the very heart of tomorrow's theatre'

That's why we read all the scripts and will continue to do so for at least another 30 years. We hope you'll be here too.

Mike Bradwell
Artistic Director

Fiona Clark
Executive Producer

Untouchable
by Simon Burt

3 – 21 December

'Tonight we keep going 'til we watch sun rise over Argos Superstore…'

Louise and Manni are eighteen, bestest friends since forever. They're going to live up town, go clubbing and get off with boys. There's only the one bed but they're sure they can work round that. They're untouchable. Nothing is ever going to come between them. Nothing…except for drink, sex and sleepy wandering hands under the duvet…

Simon Burt was born in 1975. He studied drama at Loughborough University 1994–97 and attended writing classes with the Royal Court Young Writers Programme 1999–2000. Nominated by The Bush Theatre for a place on the 2001 Performing Arts Lab Writing For Younger Audiences Workshop, *Untouchable* is his first produced play.

Book online at
www.bushtheatre.co.uk
(no booking fee)
or call
020 7610 4224

Spring 2003
14 Jan – 15 Feb
Paines Plough in association with
The Bush Theatre present
the London premiere of

Drowned World
by Gary Owen

Winner of a Fringe First and hit of the Edinburgh Fringe Festival 2002

Support The Bush

The Bush Theatre is a writers' theatre. We commission, develop and produce exclusively new plays. In addition to reading every script sent in, we commission up to seven writers each year and offer a bespoke programme of workshops and one-to-one dramaturgy to develop their plays. Our international reputation of 30 years is built on consistently producing the very best work to the very highest standard.

The search for new voices and the quest to reach as wide an audience as possible is ongoing. It is an ever-increasing challenge. We gratefully acknowledge support for our core programme from London Arts and London Borough of Hammersmith and Fulham. However, there are many individuals and companies whose generous support enables us to maintain and expand the programme of writer's development and continue to reach new young voices.

The Bush Theatre is launching a new **Patron Scheme** to coincide with its 30th Birthday season. The new scheme will offer opportunities for both Individual and Corporate Giving. Participating patrons will be able to enjoy a close relationship with the theatre in addition to receiving a wide range of benefits, which will include ticket offers and invitations to special events. This new scheme will directly support the Writers' Development Programme and help produce the new writers and new plays of the future.

Please join us in supporting another 30 years of new theatre. For full information on the **Patron Scheme**, please call Kate Mitchell, Development Manager on 020 7602 3703.

Gold Patrons of The Bush Theatre

The Agency, Giancarla Alen-Buckley, Jim Broadbent, Nick Cave, Joe Conneely, Feelgood Fiction, Ken Griffin, Albert & Lyn Fuss, Jonathan Green, Mary Hoare, ICM, Itnetwork.com, Catherine Johnson, Roy MacGregor, The Mackintosh Foundation, Michael Palin, Ralph Picken, Universal Pictures, 6th Floor Ltd, Richard Wilson, William Morris Agency (UK) Ltd, Working Title Films, Richard Zajdlic

Patrons of The Bush Theatre

Alan Brodie Representation, Alexandra Cann Representation, Conway, Van Gelder, Gillian Diamond, Paola Dionisotti, Charles Elton, Chloë Emmerson, David and Yvonna Gold, David Hare, Amanda Howard Associates, Philip Jackson, Peter Kelly and Karen Duggan, Primary Stages Theatre, New York, Marmont Management, Tim McInnerny, Stephen Nathan and Colleen Toomey, Samuel French Ltd, Rochelle Stevens & Co, Lady Warner, Richard Warner

The Bush would like to extend special thanks to the following for their support: The Mathilda and Terrence Kennedy Charitable Trust, The Olivier Foundation. This theatre has the support of the Pearson Playwrights' Scheme, sponsored by Pearson plc.

First published in 2002 by Oberon Books Ltd.
(incorporating Absolute Classics)
521 Caledonian Road, London N7 9RH
Tel: 020 7607 3637 / Fax: 020 7607 3629

e-mail: oberon.books@btinternet.com
www.oberonbooks.com

A catalogue record for this book is available from the British
Library.

ISBN: 1 84002 328 7

Cover photo: M + H Communications

Printed in Great Britain by Antony Rowe Ltd, Chippenham.

For Stella Duffy and the Walton possibilities –
past and present.
Ka aroha ahau ki a koe Stella mo ake tonu atu

Thanks to:

Pearson. Katie Haines. Mike Bradwell, Fiona Clark, Nicola Wilson, Owen Lewis, Will Kerley and everyone at the Bush. Niall Ashdown and Rebecca Armstrong for daily support. Jack Bradley, Jane Greenfield, Sandra Morris, Andy Pryor, Lee Simpson, Luke Sorba, Elizabeth Woodcraft. Jack and Esther Silas. And huge thanks to John Tiffany for being patient, for giving great advice and for making me laugh.

Characters

PETE

LINDA

GRACE

KATE

Scene 1

Spring. The living room of LINDA and PETE's garden flat in South London. A door opens on to a small patio, where pot plants stand meticulously in a line. A bag of compost is slit down the middle, dirt around the opening. There is a chrome watering can and a large upturned plant pot. The patio is covered by a small corrugated plastic roof. Rubbish has collected in the ridges. The side door to the garden is always unlocked.

PETE, thirty-eight, boyish, bit nerdy, but there's something attractive about him, is taking cuttings from a spider plant. LINDA, forty-two, lies on the sofa in her dressing gown. In a cluster at the end of the table are two bags of crisps, one open, one unopened, bowls of peanuts and olives, pint glasses and an open bottle of red wine. PETE puts the cuttings in a piece of newspaper and puts that on the table. He slides the food back into the centre of the table, stuffs a few peanuts into his mouth. He makes loud eating noises.

LINDA: Do you have to do that now Pete?

PETE: What, eat peanuts?

LINDA: That. The cutting.

PETE: I promised Grace.

LINDA: Since when do you keep your promises?

PETE: That's not fair, Linda. I'm a man of my word.

> *PETE picks up the opened bag of crisps. It's empty. PETE opens the other bag, takes a handful, offers some to LINDA. She shakes her head. He eats the crisps.*

I hope they like chicken. Do they like chicken?

LINDA: Yeah.

PETE: Do you know that for a fact, or are you guessing?

> *Beat.*

15

LINDA: Guessing.

PETE: But do you think you're right?

LINDA: I don't know. It's a guess.

PETE: You know what Grace is like. One fad after another. Last time we saw her she was a vegetarian. The time before that she was a vegan. Did you do that at her age? Change your eating habits as often as you changed your lipstick?

Beat.

LINDA: I never wore lipstick.

PETE: So?

LINDA: So what?

PETE: So what did you do?

LINDA: Took diet pills, drank black coffee, ate grapefruit, toast – no butter.

PETE: Weren't you hungry?

LINDA: Starving. But thin. After a while you don't notice the hunger.

Beat.

PETE: Are you going to put something on?

LINDA: I have.

PETE: Clothes. Shoes. Bit of mascara?

LINDA ignores him.

They'll be here any minute.

LINDA: They won't.

PETE: Yes they will. I said one o'clock. I stressed, one o'clock. It doesn't take long to get here from Clapham. Unless you're Kate and go via north London by mistake.

LINDA: She did that once.

Beat.

They'll be late. They're always late. You have to invite them an hour earlier if you want them on time.

Beat.

PETE: Bit of mascara?

LINDA: Are you telling me I look better with make-up?

PETE: No. It just makes you look more like you. Just a bit?

LINDA: Maybe.

PETE shows LINDA the cuttings.

PETE: Chlorophytum Comosum Vittatum.

LINDA: Whatever.

PETE: It gives it a whole new meaning. Chlorophytum…

Beat.

Look, I could have cancelled. Told them not to come. That you weren't up to seeing other people yet. They wouldn't have minded.

LINDA: They're family.

PETE: But you don't want to see anyone.

LINDA: Do you want to see them?

PETE: Yeah, of course. I like your sister. I like your niece. Most people hate other people's kids. I like them.

LINDA: You're weird.

Pause.

PETE: It's alright.

LINDA: I know. (*Beat.*) Come here.

PETE: Why?

LINDA: Just do it.

> *PETE moves to LINDA. She pulls him down and kisses him, gently.*

PETE: What was that for?

> *LINDA shrugs.*

I'm sorry.

LINDA: Me too.

PETE: Yeah.

LINDA: It doesn't matter.

PETE: It does. It really matters.

> *PETE's hand hovers over her stomach. LINDA grabs his hand and stops him.*

I wanted this one as much as the others.

LINDA: Yeah.

PETE: More than the others.

LINDA: Well they obviously didn't want us.

PETE: Don't say that.

LINDA: It's true. They say souls choose who they want as parents.

PETE: You talk bollocks. You know that. Absolute bloody bollocks.

LINDA: Yeah, but at least it makes sense.

PETE: Do you think they're all lined up going, 'Don't like the look of her, my room's not very nice, I'm not eating that.' The babies will come when they're ready.

LINDA: And what if they're never ready?

PETE: They will be.

Pause.

LINDA: What if they never come?

PETE: They'll come.

Beat.

LINDA: I don't know how long I can wait.

PETE: What do you mean?

After a moment, LINDA gets up. Her whole demeanour has changed.

LINDA: Pour me some wine.

PETE: Red or white?

LINDA: Red. I feel like getting pissed.

LINDA exits. PETE fills a pint glass with red wine. He empties the crisps into a bowl, eats one olive, then another. The doorbell rings. PETE doesn't know what to do with the seeds, so he spits them outside. PETE moves to the hall which is just visible to the audience. He presses a buzzer, talks into the mouthpiece in a silly voice.

PETE: The door is open.

PETE tidies the table. KATE and GRACE enter. KATE is LINDA's forty-five years old sister, overly made up, predictably dressed. GRACE is KATE's daughter. GRACE is sixteen, attractive, not slim, not fat. She has curves and she's not ashamed to show them off. No matter how grown up GRACE tries to be, we must remember, she is a child. She wears a fitted T-shirt and low cut jeans. GRACE gives PETE an opened box of chocolates.

GRACE: Left the soft centres for you.

PETE: Oh, right. Thanks. Something to look forward to. When my teeth fall out.

GRACE: Shouldn't have to wait too long then.

PETE kisses KATE. GRACE noses around.

Place looks good.

KATE: Tidy.

PETE: Well you know what we're like. (*Beat.*) Tidy.

KATE: No kids to mess the place up.

PETE: No.

GRACE: Mum!

KATE: What? Oh sorry. I didn't mean…

GRACE takes a CD out of her bag, slips it into the CD player. Puts it on loud.

Grace!

GRACE lowers the volume.

GRACE: My Mini disc's broken, what am I supposed to do? Pete always likes my music. Don't you Pete?

PETE: Yeah. She educates me.

GRACE: That's right. I educate him.

PETE: Have you seen who's coming to the Academy?

KATE: Grace isn't interested in art.

GRACE: Brixton Academy.

Beat.

PETE: Bowie.

GRACE: Yeah?

PETE: Yeah.

GRACE: You've got tickets?

PETE: Yes.

GRACE: Can I come with you?

PETE: No. Linda's his number one fan. She'd leave me for him. And you know what. I'd let her. I'd be proud.

GRACE: You're mad.

GRACE takes the bowl of crisps, sits down, starts to eat.

KATE: Where is she?

PETE: Getting dressed.

KATE: How is she?

PETE nods twice then shakes his head as he says the words –

PETE: Okay. Okay. Not good.

KATE: No. I didn't think so. You could have cancelled you know.

PETE: I said, I told her you wouldn't mind.

KATE: Of course not.

PETE: But you know what she's like.

LINDA enters and stands by the door. She's dressed, no make up.

LINDA: What am I like?

KATE goes over to LINDA, hugs and kisses her.

KATE: I've been worried about you.

LINDA: Then why didn't you call? (*Beat.*) Where's my wine?

PETE: Here.

PETE gives LINDA the pint glass of wine. He shrugs at the size of the glass.

Kate, Grace, drink?

LINDA turns to GRACE who eats non-stop. When GRACE sees LINDA she gives her a big hug.

KATE: God, she's such a pig. Sometimes I think she's got worms. She behaves like we never feed her.

PETE: Do you? (*Beat.*) Red alright?

KATE: Yes please. But not that much.

PETE: We broke all our wine glasses.

PETE glances at LINDA.

KATE: Oh. You should have said.

PETE: I just did.

KATE: We've got some spare. Twenty in fact. Mike can't resist a good bargain.

PETE: Is there such a thing as a bad bargain?

KATE: What?

PETE: Only you said…

LINDA: Stop it Pete.

PETE gives a quarter full pint glass of red wine to KATE.

KATE: Thanks.

KATE looks flirtatiously at PETE's shirt.

Gorgeous shirt.

PETE: It was a present. From Linda.

KATE: I didn't think Linda had such good taste.

LINDA: Well obviously she does.

PETE points the bottle of wine at GRACE.

GRACE: Yes please.

KATE: She shouldn't.

GRACE: She should.

PETE: She's sixteen. We were on spliffs and vodka at sixteen.

KATE: We weren't.

PETE: Oh, and what did you do?

LINDA: Bunked off school so we could go to the chip van.

PETE: (*Feigning disbelief.*) No!

KATE: There was this place called the dump. Do you remember it Linda?

PETE laughs. LINDA nods.

PETE: The dump?

KATE: Yes.

PETE: What did you do at the dump?

KATE: Nothing really. It was this bit of overgrown park, with a stream. Being caught in the middle of the dump meant detention or being made to run around the playing field while everyone else watched and laughed. I never got caught.

Beat.

PETE: I wonder if anyone ever dumped at the dump?

KATE: Probably. There were loads of old bags and things. (*Beat.*) I don't want to encourage her, not while she's studying.

PETE: One glass? One little glass. Go on.

KATE: Just one.

PETE pours, gives a glass to GRACE. GRACE increases the volume momentarily so they can all hear it, pounding.

She'll make herself deaf.

GRACE lowers the volume just as PETE says –

PETE: What?

PETE laughs, smiles at LINDA.

What are Mike and the boys up to that's more interesting than coming here?

KATE: Doing what they do. Whatever that is. Bowling or something. Grace didn't want to go. Grace, put that thing off. Grace!

PETE: Leave her, it's okay. We don't mind, do we Linda?

LINDA shakes her head.

LINDA: Course not.

They all seem uncomfortable, unsure what to say. PETE goes to the table, picks up the cuttings.

PETE: These are for Grace.

KATE: Oh.

PETE: Chlorophytum Comosum Vittatum.

KATE: It's a spider plant.

PETE: Yes, it's also commonly known as a spider plant. She said she liked it. Last time she was here.

KATE: Grace? Like something like that?

GRACE turns round.

PETE: For you.

GRACE: Chlorophytum Comosum Vittatum.

PETE: How did you know that?

GRACE: You told me last time I was here.

PETE: Yeah, but they're not the kind of words you remember.

GRACE: I do. I've got an almost photographic memory.

KATE: She has. Really. She remembers the most ridiculous things.

PETE: Oh yeah, like what?

KATE: I can't remember. She's weird.

GRACE: I am not weird. I just remember things.

PETE: You should be a detective.

GRACE: Yeah, I thought about that.

KATE: Grace be a detective? She can't even find her way home.

GRACE glares at KATE.

GRACE: Chlorophytum. I think it's quite beautiful. Poetic.

KATE: Poetic!

GRACE: Hypnotic almost, if you say it enough times.

KATE: She remembers names, faces, where she met people. It's quite embarrassing sometimes.

LINDA: Does that mean you're an A grade student?

KATE: She would be if she studied.

GRACE: I do study. You just don't see me do it.

PETE: What do you want to be when you grow up?

GRACE: Be like that gardener.

PETE: Charlie Dimmock?

GRACE: Kim Wilde. She's pretty.

PETE: Yeah.

GRACE: Dad thinks she's pretty.

PETE: In an earthy kind of way. She used to be a singer.

GRACE: Yeah, that's what dad said. Can't see it myself. She
looks better with her hands in the soil.

PETE: Yeah. (*Beat.*) Do you know what to do with it?

GRACE shrugs.

Put it in water, wait until they grow roots and then
straight into a pot. With earth. And a prayer.

GRACE: A prayer?

PETE: My mum always used to say you should pray over
things when you plant them.

KATE: I didn't know you were religious Pete?

LINDA: He's not.

GRACE: Thanks. Thanks very much for that.

PETE: I'll just go and check the lunch. Don't want to burn
it.

PETE exits.

KATE: You look well.

LINDA: Really?

KATE: How are you?

LINDA: Fine.

KATE: After your…after the…

LINDA: Miscarriage. You can say the word. Not saying it doesn't make it less painful you know.

KATE: Yeah. Your miscarriage. How are you?

LINDA: Great. Never felt better. Soon as they whipped it out of me I felt fantastic.

KATE: Well, it was a few weeks ago.

LINDA: That's right. It was a few weeks ago that they sucked the fifth foetus out of my uterus and now I feel fine. On top of the world, like I've just won the New York marathon.

KATE: When I miscarried I thought it was the end of the world. But you have to get on. I did. And now look what I've got. Three… What's for lunch?

As PETE enters –

PETE: Baby chicken.

KATE: Poussin.

PETE: Grace hasn't gone vegetarian again has she?

KATE: No. She's a carnivore. Put any lump of flesh in front of her and she'll devour it.

PETE: I hope you're hungry.

KATE: Ravenous.

PETE: Good. There's lots of it. They were two for one.

KATE: God, you're like Mike – I wouldn't be surprised if you were brothers in a past life, or separated at birth. He can't resist two for one. We've got cupboards full of washing powder, tissues, toilet roll. If there's a nuclear war, we'll be prepared.

PETE: You won't need toilet paper. (*Beat.*) Anyway, one baby chicken…

KATE: Poussin.

PETE: One poo sin each.

Pause.

KATE: How's life in the plant world, Pete?

PETE: The same. Over worked, under paid.

LINDA: But he gets free plants.

KATE: You've never given me any.

PETE: You've never asked.

KATE: How could I ask? I didn't know there was anything to ask for. I've given you things from the surgery. Things I shouldn't give you.

LINDA: Dental tape and mouth wash.

KATE: The dentists get all the good stuff.

PETE: Anything in particular you'd like?

KATE: I prefer cut flowers.

LINDA: I planted cornflowers last year. Just after the embryos had been put back.

PETE: (*To KATE.*) Transferred. They call it transferred.

LINDA: Thought we could watch them grow together. Grow your own, Kate. It's much more satisfying.

KATE: No time. The kids take up most of it. And work. And Mike. There's not a lot left for me. You can be anyone, do anything. You're lucky. So much time to do what you want.

LINDA: Yes. I often think how lucky we are.

PETE: Leave it Linda.

GRACE: Are we eating soon?

All three glare at her.

I only asked. Can I watch TV?

PETE hands her the controls. GRACE moves to the sofa, sits down.

KATE: Do you have to?

GRACE: Have you got cable?

PETE: Any channel you want.

KATE: Can't you have a conversation? You know, words.

GRACE: Yeah.

PETE: It's fine, really.

KATE: I don't know why you didn't just stay at home, if all you want to do is watch TV.

PETE tops up their wine. He sits down beside GRACE. He is aware of her body, of her breasts, full and round under her T-shirt. They watch TV together. The following conversations are simultaneous, but KATE and LINDA can't hear GRACE and PETE and vice versa. / denotes the end of one sequence of dialogue.

I wanted to talk to you.

LINDA: What about?

KATE: Grace. /

GRACE: I've had a man's cock in my mouth.

PETE: What?

GRACE: A man's cock. In my mouth. Does that disgust you? /

LINDA: What about her?

KATE: She's seeing someone. Some boy. /

GRACE: I thought it might. /

LINDA: That's nice. /

PETE: Was it nice? I mean…oh fuck.

GRACE: Did that as well. /

KATE: He's older than her. /

GRACE: Yeah. Nice. Really nice. Tasty. /

LINDA: How do you know?

KATE: She told me. /

Simultaneously.

PETE: Anyone I know?

LINDA: Anyone I know? /

GRACE: No. /

KATE: My sixteen-year-old daughter is having an affair with someone twice her age.

LINDA: He's thirty two?

KATE: He's eighteen. That's what she says. /

GRACE: He's eighteen.

LINDA: What does he do?

KATE: Nothing by the sounds of it. I don't know what to do. I feel totally helpless. She thinks I don't care. She thinks I don't have time for her.

LINDA: Do you?

KATE: Yeah. /

GRACE: I'm in love with him. /

KATE: She's in love with him. /

GRACE: I think I'm in love with him. /

KATE: She thinks she's in love with him. How can she be? /

GRACE: I know what you're thinking. /

KATE: How can a sixteen year old know what it's like to be in love? In lust, maybe.

LINDA: What does Mike think? /

PETE: What's your dad say? /

KATE: He doesn't know. He'd kill her. He'd kill him. He'd probably kill me as well. You know what he's like. Traditional old bastard. Sometimes I wonder why I married him. /

PETE: Grace? /

LINDA: Are you going to tell him? Are you going to tell Mike?

KATE: Of course not.

GRACE speaks to everyone.

GRACE: Can we eat? I'm starving.

KATE: Hardly starving. You don't know the meaning of starving.

GRACE: Don't lecture me.

KATE: I was only going to say that you kids…

GRACE: I'm not a kid…

KATE: …miss one meal and you think your throat's been cut. Try and not eat for a week, a month, see how hungry you feel then.

GRACE: Oh, and you'd know about that, would you?

LINDA: Pete?

PETE: Soon.

GRACE holds out the empty crisp bowl.

GRACE: Any more of these?

KATE: You'll be sick.

GRACE: Got any flavoured ones?

PETE: Rosemary and Sea Salt. Garlic and Sun Dried Tomatoes. Prawn cocktail.

GRACE: Got any Marmite ones?

KATE: Grace.

GRACE: Got any Marmite ones…please?

PETE: I'll see what I can find.

GRACE: I've had Marmite flavoured condoms. Bit too strong.

PETE exits. LINDA and KATE glare at GRACE.

What you looking at?

Simultaneously.

KATE: You.

LINDA: Nothing.

Pause.

KATE: Do you think you'll try again?

Beat.

LINDA: You know. I might stop.

KATE: Stop? You can't stop.

LINDA: I want to get on with my life.

KATE: What about Pete?

LINDA: I haven't told Pete.

KATE: Oh.

LINDA: They weren't so good this time. The embryos. Lower grade. Only one. I've always had higher. Time before this I had three.

KATE: You could have had triplets.

LINDA: Yeah. I could have had triplets.

KATE: That would have been fun.

> *Beat.*

But it didn't work.

LINDA: Nothing's worked. I've tried it all. Acupuncture, Homeopathy, Chinese Herbs that made me vomit. Body balancing, Aromatherapy. I cut out alcohol, salt, caffeine. And chocolate. I don't even smoke.

KATE: There's no logic to it is there. I mean, I wasn't bothered about having kids, ate and drank, and smoked and look what I ended up with. Three great big pains in the arse.

LINDA: I took it for granted. Thought it was always possible, that I was special, different. But I'm not. I'm just like everyone else.

KATE: It's a shock, isn't it, when you discover you're just like the person sitting next to you.

> *GRACE's mobile goes off to the theme of EastEnders. GRACE picks up the phone as PETE enters with the packet of crisps.*

PETE: Best I could do.

GRACE: I hate Salt and Vinegar.

PETE: Thank you.

GRACE whispers into the phone as she exits.

KATE: It's him.

LINDA: Who?

KATE: That boy.

LINDA: How do you know?

KATE: I know. It's him.

PETE: What boy?

LINDA: Grace is seeing someone.

PETE: Oh. Have you met him?

KATE: She won't let me. She won't even tell me his name. She thinks I'll get too involved.

LINDA: You will.

KATE: I'm not that bad am I?

Beat.

PETE: No. No of course not.

KATE: It's just the thought of her…

LINDA: Sex?

KATE: Making love.

PETE: Shagging.

LINDA: You'll have to get used to it.

KATE: I know. Just not yet.

PETE: You did it. Still do I presume.

KATE: Of course.

PETE: I bet Mike's a bit of a goer.

KATE: He has his moments.

PETE: I bet he does.

Pause.

Do you do anything different?

LINDA: Pete!

KATE: Like what?

PETE: You know, different?

KATE: He used a fish slice once to swat a fly. Ended up breaking a china dog my aunt gave us. I suppose that's different. Is that what you meant?

LINDA: Yeah, that's what he meant.

PETE: A fish slice?

KATE: I wouldn't have minded, only I was cooking at the time, and when he swung it around bits of haddock flew off the edges like kamikaze flies.

GRACE offstage laughs loudly. They all turn to look at where the laughter has come from. Lights down.

Scene 2

Later. The garden. PETE sits on an upturned plant pot smoking. GRACE stands beside him, cigarette in mouth. She seems nervous.

GRACE: I'm dying for a pee.

PETE: Go on then.

GRACE: Can't be bothered. (*Beat.*) Do you pee in the garden?

PETE: No.

GRACE: But you could.

PETE: I don't. I wouldn't.

GRACE: Worried the neighbours will see you?

PETE: Worried I'll kill my plants.

GRACE: I hate public toilets.

PETE: We don't have public toilets.

GRACE: I hate it when people piss on seats.

PETE: I thought only men did that?

GRACE: At least you've got an excuse.

PETE: What's that then?

GRACE: You're all blind when it comes to peeing.

PETE: It's not as easy as it looks.

GRACE: How hard can it be? It's not as if you're bringing a plane in to land. (*Beat.*) Everyone's scared they'll catch something, so they don't sit down. They hover above it, bums like vultures circling the air. Only they miss their prey. The worst ones are the ones who don't wipe up, so you enter a cubicle to pale yellow drops of piss. And when there's no paper, and if you don't have any tissues, you have to do the same. Can't sit on someone else's piss, can you? And then the person after you thinks you did it on purpose. But you can't explain. You can't say, right in the middle of a public toilet, it was like this before and there's no loo paper and I didn't have any tissues.

PETE blows smoke rings into the air. GRACE copies him.

PETE: You shouldn't be doing that.

GRACE: Making circles?

PETE: Smoking.

GRACE: I can make squares if you like.

GRACE drops her cigarette, crushes it with the sole of her shoe.

Light me another one.

PETE: It's bad for you.

GRACE: Then why do you do it?

PETE shrugs.

PETE: My goods are already damaged.

GRACE: Light me another one. Please.

PETE lights another cigarette, hands it to GRACE.

It's nice out here.

PETE: Could be better.

Pause.

GRACE: How many have you had today?

PETE: This is my first. Linda doesn't like me smoking in the flat.

GRACE: You mean she doesn't let you.

Pause.

PETE: Did you really have…Marmite flavoured condoms?

GRACE looks at him, shakes her head slowly, then nods.

Beat.

GRACE: Do you and Linda have sex a lot?

PETE: Sorry?

GRACE: Do you and Linda have sex a lot? Do you fuck, make love, shag, do it?

PETE: What kind of a question is that?

GRACE: A personal one.

PETE: Yeah, well it's none of your business.

GRACE: I bet you do. All the time. Like rabbits. Do you?

PETE: No. Yes. Sometimes. Depends.

GRACE: I'll take the first answer.

PETE: Why do you want to know?

GRACE: Just wondered.

Pause.

PETE: We haven't…much…recently. Because of the babies.

GRACE: Oh.

PETE: She…Linda doesn't like me touching her. She's had a lot of people around her, you know, being intrusive.

GRACE: Has it been hard for you?

PETE: Yeah. But it's not happening to my body, so I don't get treated the same way as Linda.

GRACE: What about adoption?

PETE: It's not the same.

GRACE: There are loads of unwanted kids around. Couldn't you have one of them?

PETE: It's not that easy Grace.

GRACE: You want a kid don't you?

PETE: Yeah.

GRACE: Will you try again?

PETE: Of course. And I think it might work next time. I've got a feeling.

GRACE: And what if it doesn't?

PETE: It will.

Beat.

GRACE: I don't think my parents do.

PETE: What?

GRACE: Have sex. (*Beat.*) I have.

PETE: I know.

GRACE: Had sex.

PETE: You said.

GRACE: So.

PETE: So?

GRACE: It was good.

PETE: Good.

GRACE: It was great.

PETE: Great.

Pause.

GRACE: Do you want to have sex?

PETE: What?

GRACE: Do you want to have sex? (*Beat.*) With me?

PETE doesn't answer. Keeps smoking.

You're not bad looking you know.

PETE: Thanks very much.

GRACE: For an older man.

PETE: I'm not an older man.

GRACE: You're older than me.

PETE: So?

GRACE: So you're an older man.

PETE: I thought you had a boyfriend?

GRACE: Mum tell you?

PETE: Yeah.

GRACE: She can't keep her mouth shut.

PETE: She's your mother. She cares about you.

GRACE: Yeah. Right.

Beat.

Don't you want to know about him? My boyfriend.

PETE: If you want to tell me.

GRACE: He's young.

PETE: You said.

GRACE: Very knowing.

PETE: Really.

GRACE: Clever.

PETE: Right.

Beat.

GRACE: He knows a lot about sex. (*Beat.*) Do you want to?

PETE: No.

GRACE: I'm good.

PETE: I'm sure you are.

GRACE: Why not then?

PETE: I'm a married man.

GRACE: You're not married.

PETE: In a long-term relationship.

GRACE: Don't you find me attractive?

PETE: Of course.

GRACE: Well then?

PETE stubs out his cigarette, does a bit of weeding. GRACE smiles, stubs out her cigarette, starts to help him –

Scene 3

Later. PETE is outside, lying on the ground, eyes closed. GRACE stares into space. LINDA and KATE enter the living room with glasses of wine. Half a lemon meringue pie is on the table.

KATE: I'm meant to understand. I am supposed to be understanding.

LINDA: You can't understand. Not really.

KATE: I'm trying.

LINDA: I know. But you can't understand what it feels like. To not be able to have something you want so much. To wake every day wishing you'd made different choices, that someone had told you, warned you that you can't have it all. That you never could. It's just not possible.

KATE: No.

LINDA: The other day, in Sainsbury's, this woman started shouting at her kid, a baby, about a year old. Its dummy had fallen, slipped out of its mouth, you know, by accident. And the woman got hold of it and shoved it back in really hard. And then she lifted her hand up and her fingers slapped the side of its face. 'Don't do that,' she said. 'Don't do that.' And the baby giggled and smiled and the dummy started to slip again and I could see her hand going up. And I stared at her, like, 'what do you think you're doing?' And she looked at me and pulled back her hand and laughed and said, 'kids, you know what they're like.' (*Beat.*) Sometimes I'll stare at the garden and imagine kids, our kids, running around in the summer, bare feet dragging along the grass, sticky fingers and big toothy smiles. Or I'll see a heavily pregnant woman and want it to be me, want to know how it feels. To have that inside you. To be special, so people know you're growing something new inside you. To have a fuss made, to never be the same person again, to have a new identity, to be a mother, a mum. And it hurts. It hurts to know I'll never be that special. That my special time has run out.

Pause.

KATE: I sat opposite this old man on the tube the other day. He was really small. Bird features. He wore a black beret. He had the rosiest cheeks, like someone had brushed his face with blusher. And a walking stick. And his hands were wrinkled, with big brown spots. And I sat back in my seat, a lump at the back of my throat, and I thought back to when I was sixteen, when I was so sure I'd never be as old as my parents. And when I got to thirty, I was so sure I'd never be as old as my parents. And now I'm forty-five and both my parents are dead. And I know the truth. And suddenly, looking at that old man on the Central Line I became terrified.

Pause.

You can have one of my eggs.

LINDA: And do what, make an omelette?

KATE: Scrambled eggs.

LINDA: You're too old.

KATE: Too old?

LINDA: Under thirty-five. That's the limit.

KATE: But I'm your sister, I have three children, healthy children.

LINDA: Doesn't matter. You're too old. I asked.

KATE: Bet if you went privately they'd let you do it. You can do anything if you pay.

LINDA: You're too old. Your eggs are past their sell by date.

Pause.

KATE: You're right. I am too old. (*Beat.*) I missed a period.

LINDA: What?

KATE: I missed a period. Four actually.

LINDA: You're not…?

KATE: Oh God no.

LINDA: Oh.

KATE: Although I think Mike would like it. He likes babies. I think he quite fancies himself as an older father.

Beat.

Grace volunteered.

LINDA: To do what?

KATE: Donate an egg.

LINDA: Easter twice in one day. Grace offered to do that?

KATE: Yeah. I know. I was pretty amazed. Sometimes I think she prefers you to me.

LINDA: She's too young. You're…too old and she's too young. Anyway, I couldn't put her through it. Not at her age. Her hormones are all over the place.

KATE: You're telling me. She's moody as hell. Drives her brothers insane. She argues with me all the time.

LINDA: Why?

KATE: I think she resents me.

LINDA: What for?

KATE: Not being the mother she wants. Don't tell her I told you. About the eggs.

LINDA: Of course not.

KATE: She'll get embarrassed.

LINDA: I won't mention it.

KATE: And then she'll hate me even more. I said you wouldn't let her, even if it was possible, and that it was a very lovely thought, but to forget about it and concentrate on her GCSE's.

LINDA: You're right.

KATE: Look, sometimes, it just happens. I know couples who've been trying for years, changed their life styles. And nothing. And then, then when they've forgotten all about it, when they're back on the booze and the nicotine and ready to retire, magic happens.

LINDA: I'm not sure I want magic anymore.

Pause.

The first time I miscarried, someone said, it wasn't really a baby so it didn't count. I was nine weeks. I had something alive inside me. Something growing inside me. In my body. Not the right way, but it was still growing. I saw the flash of light, its tiny heart like a glow-worm warming itself in me. And then it went out. (*Beat.*) And they said it didn't count.

GRACE enters from the garden. During the next few lines, PETE gets up, enters the lounge. He picks at the lemon meringue pie.

GRACE: Can we go home?

KATE: Soon?

GRACE: Can we go home?

KATE: You stink of smoke. Have you been smoking?

GRACE: (*To PETE.*) Have I been smoking?

PETE shrugs.

KATE: Who's side are you on?

PETE: My own.

KATE: Have you been smoking?

GRACE: What if I have? They're my lungs, I'll do what I want. (*Beat.*) Thanks for lunch.

GRACE goes to exit.

KATE: Where are you going?

GRACE: To see my lover. To get laid. To have a fuck.

GRACE exits.

Lights down.

Scene 4

Later that night. As the lights come up, we see LINDA lying on the sofa, her eyes closed. PETE is standing over her. He holds a plate with a sandwich on it, some grapes and a cup of tea. He picks at the grapes one at a time.

PETE: I thought you might be hungry.

LINDA: If it's mine then why are you eating it?

PETE swallows quickly.

PETE: I'm not.

LINDA: I can't believe you're still hungry.

PETE: I'm not.

LINDA: You had a huge lunch.

PETE: That was ages ago.

LINDA: What is it with men and food? And sex. It's like you take all you can, fill yourselves up, sleep it off and start all over again.

PETE: I wish.

LINDA opens her eyes, sits up, looks at PETE.

You look terrible.

LINDA: Thanks very much.

PETE: Do you want me to leave you alone?

LINDA: Yeah. No.

Pause.

PETE: Are you going to eat this?

LINDA: Not hungry. (*Beat.*) I wanted to be pregnant.

PETE: We'll try again.

LINDA: I wanted to be special.

PETE: You are special.

LINDA: We're a family.

PETE: Yeah.

LINDA: You and me.

PETE: You and me.

PETE puts the plate down, does 'stones papers scissors'. He does three with his fists closed and on the forth he opens his hands, laughs as he does one that resembles a rocking cradle, palm faces up, his fingers bent and together. LINDA watches him, joins him. Together they make a ball with their fists, punch them into the air three times and make the same cradle.

Silly babies.

LINDA: Stupid babies.

PETE: They had their chance.

LINDA: And they gave it up.

PETE: Don't want them.

LINDA: Never did.

PETE: Stupid babies.

LINDA: Silly babies.

PETE: You had your chance.

LINDA: And you fucked up.

PETE: Big time.

LINDA: Big time.

Pause.

PETE: They would have had a good home.

LINDA: The best home.

PETE: Cartoons.

LINDA: Egg and chips.

PETE: Brown sauce.

LINDA: Tomato ketchup.

PETE: So much love.

LINDA: So much love.

Simultaneously.

PETE: Yeah.

LINDA: Yeah.

PETE: Building sandcastles.

LINDA: And knocking them down.

PETE: Yeah.

LINDA: Yeah. (*Beat.*) Who will lick the spoon when I bake cakes?

PETE: You never bake cakes.

LINDA: I would have, if I had someone to lick the spoon.

PETE: I'll lick the spoon.

LINDA: Okay. I'll bake the cakes.

They take a moment, do 'stones paper scissors' again, but this time they don't finish it.

I want to stop trying Pete.

PETE: What?

LINDA: I want to get on, do something different with my life.

PETE: Give up on the babies?

LINDA: Yeah.

PETE: Give up on the babies?

LINDA: I was thinking about Grace…

PETE: You can't give up on the babies.

LINDA: …how she's got her whole life ahead of her, and I was jealous. I am jealous. Jealous of all her possibilities.

PETE: What about me?

LINDA: We have to look at where we are Pete, and how we got here. We can either keep dreaming about all the what ifs and the maybes and the if onlys. Or we can look at what we've got, at the positive side to all the negatives. And we can move forwards. Do all the things we've been putting on hold, in case the babies came, in case they surprised us. I'm ready to move forwards. I want to move on. We could put our things in storage, travel…

PETE: What, give up my business?

LINDA: Yes. No. Maybe.

PETE: I've only just got established.

LINDA: We could do something useful, go abroad, be helpful. Change people's lives.

PETE: I don't want to change people's lives.

LINDA: What about changing our lives?

PETE: I like my life.

LINDA: If we can't have kids, we'll have a holiday.

PETE: We've had a holiday.

LINDA: A bigger holiday. Somewhere we've always wanted to go.

PETE: I've never wanted to go anywhere. I'm happy staying here.

LINDA: Well I have.

PETE: You never told me.

LINDA: You never asked.

PETE: Where would you go?

LINDA: India, South America. Sail down the Nile. Walk to the base camp of Mount Everest.

PETE: You'd need to be fit.

LINDA: I'll get fit.

PETE: You'll be doing it without me.

LINDA: It's only an idea.

PETE: You need time.

LINDA: I've had time.

PETE: To think this through properly.

LINDA: I've had five miscarriages, eleven embryos. How many more do we need?

PETE: But the next one could be it.

LINDA: And maybe it won't. I can't go through it again.

PETE: We should think about adoption.

LINDA: No.

PETE: But Linda…

LINDA: It's not what I want.

PETE: Just think about it.

LINDA: I have thought about it. But you assume it's so easy. We want a baby, we go out, tell some organisation, a bunch of total strangers, that we can't have our own, that we've been trying for seven years, naturally, with help, with assistance from anyone they care to mention, but sorry, we can't produce. So please can you give us a child. Preferably a baby, under six months, brand new would be best, two weeks old, two days, actually how about barely out of its mother's womb? I don't want a room full of strangers deciding whether we're good enough to be parents.

PETE: We're good enough.

LINDA: Whether *they* think we're good enough to be parents.

PETE: We're good enough. (*Beat.*) I thought you wanted a baby?

LINDA: I do. But I want my life more.

PETE blows out his cheeks, starts to eat. He makes slurping noises.

Do you have to?

PETE: What? Eat? Yes, I do. It's very nice, you should try it. I make good sandwiches.

LINDA: Make those noises. (*Beat.*) Can I have a bite?

PETE: What's the magic word?

LINDA: Just give me the sandwich.

PETE: Come on.

LINDA goes to grab it.

How about dinner out tonight? You and me.

LINDA: Okay.

PETE: I fancy Thai.

LINDA: I fancy you.

PETE: Do you?

LINDA: Yeah.

PETE: You haven't said that for a while.

LINDA: Well I do.

PETE: Okay.

LINDA: Okay.

PETE: Okay.

LINDA: You do love me?

PETE: Of course.

LINDA: Even if I can't have kids?

PETE: Even if *we* can't have kids.

LINDA: You're not the problem.

PETE: It's our problem.

LINDA: It's mine. It's about me. It's about my body.

PETE: It affects me too. (*Beat.*) We could try another clinic.

LINDA: No.

PETE: We could.

LINDA: We've spent too much already.

PETE: We'll take out another loan.

LINDA: No.

PETE: I'll do whatever you want.

LINDA: I want to stop. I have to stop sometime.

PETE: When it's right for you. It's not my body being filled with pregnant women's piss.

LINDA: Pete!

PETE: And post-menopausal women's piss.

LINDA: Don't.

PETE: I keep thinking of all those women, all those pregnant women, pissing into special loos. I mean, how can you be sure they're all really pregnant? Is there someone on the door, checking. Checking all those pregnant and post-menopausal women, pissing for women like you.

LINDA: I never thought of it like that.

PETE: Yeah, well I have. I've read every inch of every leaflet. Half a dozen times. In the hope I'll find a clue, a reason why it's not working.

LINDA: It's not working because it's not working.

PETE: But it works for everyone else.

LINDA: Not everyone.

PETE: Everyone we know. Why not us?

LINDA shrugs, shakes her head. PETE looks downhearted.

LINDA: You won't leave me?

PETE: Never.

LINDA: You won't go off with a twenty-five-year-old and have her babies like all those middle-aged male celebrities?

PETE: No.

LINDA: Because you can.

PETE: I wouldn't.

LINDA: But you can.

PETE: I could also piss in the garden.

LINDA: But you might. I love you. I want to be with you.

PETE: Even when you're telling me to piss off?

LINDA: Especially when I'm telling you to piss off.

PETE: Yeah?

LINDA: Yeah.

PETE: Then give us a kiss.

LINDA: Okay.

> *LINDA kisses PETE. And again, and this time it's a long, lingering kiss.*

PETE: I got propositioned by a teenager the other day.

LINDA: Oh yeah?

PETE: Yeah.

LINDA: What did you say?

PETE: I said I was a married man.

LINDA: You're not married.

PETE: In a long-term relationship. I'll book a table.

> *PETE turns to go.*

LINDA: Pete. What if this really is it? What if I don't want to try anymore? What if I want us to move on, get on with our lives? No more talk of babies.

PETE: Then we won't talk about babies anymore.

> *PETE exits. LINDA walks over to a full-length mirror and stares at herself. She gets a cushion from the sofa, tucks it under her shirt – holds it to her body tightly.*

> (*Off.*) They can't do anything before nine. Is that alright? (*Beat.*) Linda?

LINDA: Yeah. Fine.

> *LINDA rips the pillow out from under her shirt, throws it down on the floor. PETE enters on the phone, his hand over the mouthpiece.*

PETE: They can only do nine.

LINDA: Fine. I said fine.

PETE removes his hand from the mouthpiece.

PETE: Yeah. That's fine. Pete Hunter. Okay. Bye.

PETE hangs up. Looks at LINDA, sees the cushion on the floor. He picks it up, holds it. Lights fade.

Scene 5

An evening a few weeks later. The back doors are open. An outside light shines down on the patio. PETE wears shorts and a T shirt. His hair is ruffled. There is a pile of school exercise books on the table. GRACE stands by the door, holding a back pack. KATE stands beside her.

KATE: Sorry to disturb you Pete.

PETE: It's no problem.

KATE: You weren't in the middle of anything? You know…

GRACE: Sex. She means sex.

KATE: Grace!

GRACE: I've got exams coming up, I need a break.

KATE: So do I.

GRACE: Then this is a good idea.

KATE: You could have asked me, discussed it first.

GRACE: What's to discuss? I need peace and quiet to study.

KATE: It's quiet at home.

GRACE: If you think that's quiet you must be deaf.

PETE smiles at GRACE.

KATE: We should talk.

GRACE: There's nothing to say.

KATE: You can't just turn up on someone's doorstep. They might not want you.

LINDA enters in a dressing gown.

GRACE: They do.

KATE: They might just be being polite.

GRACE: They said it was okay.

KATE: Did they?

LINDA: They did.

KATE: When?

LINDA: She called. A few days ago.

KATE: Why didn't you mention it?

GRACE shrugs.

And you're staying for a week?

GRACE: Yeah.

KATE: Only a week?

GRACE: Where am I sleeping?

PETE: Well, it's a two bedroom flat, and you know which one's ours.

GRACE: I meant…I know Linda uses the other one as a study. I could sleep in here. I'd keep it tidy.

LINDA: It's okay. Pete…

PETE: Come on. I'll show you where everything is.

GRACE and PETE exit.

LINDA: She'll be fine.

KATE: She's not a child.

LINDA: I thought she was. She just needs a change. They do. Occasionally. Need to get away. Need to do things differently.

KATE: Do they?

LINDA: Yes.

KATE: And you'd know?

LINDA: Actually yes, I would.

KATE: Don't let her sleep in.

LINDA: I won't.

KATE: And in bed by eleven.

LINDA: Eleven?

KATE: Twelve then.

LINDA: I was thinking more of ten.

KATE: Ten? How old do you think she is?

LINDA: She's studying for her GCSEs.

KATE: She stays awake all night at home. Works all night.

LINDA: That's what she tells you.

KATE: You're sure you don't mind?

LINDA: It's only for a week.

KATE: Right then.

LINDA: Do you want some tea?

KATE: No, thanks.

KATE moves to the door, calls out –

Bye Grace.

She waits a moment, hoping GRACE will respond. Nothing.

Tell her I said bye. And to call if she needs anything.

LINDA: Sure.

KATE exits. A moment later GRACE enters with a mini disc collection. She shows her mini disc player to LINDA.

GRACE: Dad got it fixed. (*Beat.*) Thanks. For covering.

LINDA: It's what aunts are for.

GRACE: I thought you didn't like being called aunt?

LINDA: Exceptional circumstance.

GRACE: I would have called. I meant to call.

LINDA: But you're more spontaneous than that?

GRACE: Sort of. Do you think Pete minds?

LINDA: Did he say he did?

GRACE: No.

LINDA: Because he would. If it bothered him, he'd tell you.

GRACE: Okay.

LINDA: Besides, he really likes you.

GRACE: That's good. I like him too. He's given me the password to his computer. Said I could use it. For research. (*Beat.*) You're lucky.

LINDA: What for?

GRACE: Having someone who loves you so much.

LINDA: Yeah. (*Beat.*) If you want to bring anyone back, that's okay.

GRACE: What do you mean?

LINDA: Your mystery boyfriend. If you're still seeing him.

GRACE: Yeah. It's been a while now. Longest relationship I've ever had.

LINDA: How's it going?

GRACE: Alright.

LINDA: Great.

GRACE: You don't mind?

LINDA: Why should I? If you're happy and he's not hurting you...

GRACE: Why should he hurt me?

LINDA: Do you love him?

GRACE shrugs.

GRACE: Dunno.

LINDA: Have you had sex?

GRACE: Yeah.

LINDA: Is it good?

GRACE: That's personal.

LINDA: Sorry.

GRACE: Fucking brilliant. You know they say you always remember your first. Well, I will.

LINDA: Has he got a name?

GRACE: No. Well yes. But no.

LINDA: Well what do you call him? You must have a name for him?

GRACE: Yeah, I do.

LINDA: What does everyone else call him?

GRACE shrugs.

GRACE: His name.

LINDA: We've got porn names.

GRACE: First pet's name and mother's maiden name?

LINDA nods excitedly.

LINDA: I'm Dotty Star and Pete is…Dynamite Walker. Hamster and tadpole.

GRACE: I'm Gorgeous Parker.

LINDA: The tabby with four white paws?

GRACE nods.

I loved her.

Pause.

GRACE: You got any rules?

LINDA: Rules? What kind of rules?

GRACE: I don't know. House rules. Lights out at ten.

LINDA: It's not a boarding school.

GRACE: I've got this friend, Emma. You'd like her. She's mad.

LINDA: Thanks.

GRACE: No, mad as in interesting, different, not mad insane. Anyway, her mum makes you take off your shoes the minute you enter the house and put on these funny black slippers. I always feel like I'm in a martial arts movie when I'm round there. She says she doesn't want other people's negative energy entering her house.

LINDA: You can do what you want, within reason. We're pretty easy going.

GRACE: You'd make a great mum.

LINDA: Thanks.

GRACE: No, I mean it. You would. You should know that.

LINDA: Yeah well.

GRACE: And just because you're not…doesn't mean you don't matter. Doesn't mean you're not great just as you are.

LINDA: I know.

GRACE: In case you don't. You matter to me. To a lot of people. Being a mother doesn't make you matter any more.

> *Beat.*

LINDA: Want a drink?

GRACE: Coke please.

LINDA: I thought something more intoxicating.

GRACE: What, like wine?

LINDA: Malibu and pineapple. I bought some last time you were here. I forgot about it.

GRACE: Is that what you think all sixteen-year-olds drink? (*Beat.*) Coke would be good.

> *LINDA exits. GRACE looks around. Picks up photos of PETE and LINDA. She runs her hand along a sideboard, looks at her finger. No dust.*

> *GRACE opens cupboards, starts looking through drawers. She takes out a video. On the side is a white strip with LINDA PARKER written in black felt pen.*

As LINDA enters with a glass of coke –

LINDA: Here you are.

GRACE quickly puts the tape back in the drawer, closes it, picks up an exercise book as LINDA enters. LINDA gives the coke to GRACE.

GRACE: Great.

LINDA: There are crisps if you want?

GRACE: I've given them up. (*Beat.*) How's school?

LINDA: I was just about to ask you that. Working hard?

GRACE: Yes. No.

LINDA: We'll both be out during the day so you can get a lot done.

GRACE: Are the kids good. At your school? Are they good?

LINDA: What at? Work?

GRACE: Life.

LINDA: Some of them.

GRACE: Is it hard? Teaching kids when you want them so much?

LINDA: I don't want those kids. I want my own. I look at other people's kids and I don't want them. I want mine. Look, I've got a load of marking to do tonight.

GRACE: Want any help? Red's my favourite colour. (*Beat.*) Want to know what I want to be when I grow up?

LINDA: I thought you were grown up?

GRACE: Where did you meet Pete?

LINDA: At a party. And you? Your boy with no name. Where did you meet him?

GRACE: At an eighties party.

LINDA: I hated the eighties.

GRACE: Eighty-six was a good year.

LINDA: Tell me more.

GRACE: About the eighties?

LINDA: About this boy.

GRACE: He asked me out. I said yes. We shagged, sorry, we had sex. End of story.

LINDA: And?

GRACE: And what?

LINDA: Was it everything you thought it would be?

GRACE is becoming uneasy.

GRACE: Yeah, of course. Why shouldn't it be?

LINDA: Because it isn't always.

GRACE: How was it for you?

LINDA: The first time I made love?

GRACE: You made love?

LINDA: He was six years older than me, a friend of the family who lived next door. I was eighteen. Terrified. We did it in a hotel.

GRACE: Did he have a name? This man.

LINDA: Frank. Frank… I never knew his last name. My parents were away for a weekend. He took me out for dinner. He asked them first. It was the most romantic meal I've ever had. I never thought fried onions were sexy until that night. He was charming, said all the right things. After the meal, he drove me to the river. For a moment I thought he was going to kill me and dump my body in the water. He'd booked a room with a river view. He was gentle and sweet and…

GRACE: The onions were better?

LINDA: I had nothing to compare it to. It was what it was. But I wasn't touched. And I wanted to be. I really wanted it to matter. I wanted him to think I was grown up, sophisticated.

GRACE: And what did he want?

LINDA: Sex.

GRACE: You said you made love.

LINDA: I made love, he had sex.

Pause.

GRACE: It hurt. The first time. I didn't think it would. But it did. Then he lit up a fag and stared at the ceiling for ten minutes while I lay there, unsure what to do next. Second time was better. Slower. He took more care of me. (*Beat.*) Where's Pete?

LINDA: Probably e-mailing sad jokes to the world.

GRACE: Thanks Linda. For letting me stay.

LINDA: Make yourself at home. If you can't find something, ask.

LINDA picks up her exercise books.

GRACE: Don't be too hard on them.

LINDA exits. GRACE waits a few seconds. She goes back to the drawer, removes the video, all the time ensuring no one is coming. She slips it in, switches it on. There is no sound. GRACE is mesmerised. Lights fade gradually as GRACE watches. PETE appears by the door. He watches for a couple of seconds.

PETE: That's private.

GRACE: It was already in there.

PETE: It wasn't. How long have you been watching it?

GRACE shrugs.

PETE: I suppose it magicked its way in there?

GRACE: No.

PETE: It's private.

GRACE: Sorry.

PETE: It could have been anything.

GRACE: It's got her name on it.

PETE: Yeah, which means it's Linda's.

GRACE: And yours.

Pause.

PETE: Every now and again Linda will watch, just to remember, to see those little cells before they put them back.

GRACE: Transferred. You said they called it transferring them. They're so tiny.

PETE: Smaller than tiny. Like dust on newly painted wood.

GRACE: Beautiful.

PETE: Yeah. Beautiful. Works of art. Hard to believe what they grow in to. They got stuck once, in the syringe. Wouldn't go in. Dr had to try four times before they shot up. And when they did, I yelled, we have take off.

GRACE: What's it like? Being there, seeing them?

PETE: The first time was really strange. Linda lay there, in this hot room with a bright light shining directly in her face. They said bring a video if you like, we'll tape them before they…get transferred. Some people like to tape them. Linda didn't want to, said it was stupid, they were only cells and what would she want to tape them for. She'd have a baby anyway. She didn't need a video of embryos. I knew she'd change her mind, so I slipped a cassette into her bag. They show them to you on this screen. It's totally white and then all of a sudden, they're there in front of you. Living. Life. The life we created together. Magnified loads of times so they look big and strong. We cried the first time. All those injections and Linda's legs, bruised because I'm a clumsy sod with needles. All that and we saw the end product. Most people don't get to see that. That's special. The doctor said this is the moment when some people give them names. And Linda said that one's Molly and that one's Eli. And they were, for four weeks, until she woke up one morning to stomach cramp and specks of blood. We even spoke to them. Sounds mad doesn't it? We had conversations in the dark, at night. We made plans, chose the colour of their room, and in our heads we'd even picked the beds they'd sleep in. Bunk beds. We passed shops and said, that's for Molly and that's for Eli. (*Beat.*) The second time we called them something else, thought they weren't coming to us because they didn't like their names.

GRACE: What did you call them?

PETE: Emily, James and George. After that we stopped naming them.

GRACE: But you videoed them?

PETE: Yeah. All eleven of them. This is all Linda has.

GRACE: I'm really sorry.

PETE: Don't let her see you with it Grace.

GRACE: I won't.

PETE turns to exit.

Pete.

PETE stops. GRACE walks up to him, kisses him on the cheek.

PETE: What was that for?

GRACE: Because I love you.

PETE kisses her back.

PETE: I love you too Grace.

They look at each other for a moment.

PETE exits. Lights down on GRACE.

Scene 6

The lounge at LINDA and PETE's. Early evening. LINDA is reading. GRACE enters. She carries a bunch of flowers. She hands them to LINDA. Every time LINDA tries to read, GRACE interrupts her.

LINDA: What are these for?

GRACE: Having me stay so long. I wanted to say thank you.

LINDA: There was no need.

GRACE: I'll put them in water shall I?

LINDA: Thanks.

LINDA continues to read.

GRACE: Interesting?

LINDA: Necessary.

GRACE: I don't like reading.

LINDA: I didn't when I was your age. Then when I was in my early twenties, something happened. I discovered books. This whole new world opened up. Somewhere I could hide.

Pause.

GRACE: What time's mum coming over?

LINDA: Soon.

GRACE: Are we having fish and chips?

LINDA: Indian.

GRACE: Great.

Pause.

You and Pete, you're so young.

LINDA: Right.

GRACE: I don't mean in age, I mean in your heads. It's a compliment.

LINDA: Thanks.

GRACE: Where is he?

LINDA: He's got an interview in the city. For a new contract.

GRACE: Lots of money?

LINDA: More than he's been earning. He might even have to employ someone.

GRACE: Great, I need a job.

Pause.

Something happened to me.

LINDA: Oh yeah? (*Beat.*) Has someone hurt you?

GRACE shakes her head.

What then?

GRACE: For the first time in my life, someone said they loved me.

LINDA: What it nice?

GRACE: Yes.

LINDA: Who said the magic words?

GRACE: A bloke. I love you Grace. That's what he said. I love you.

LINDA: Your bloke? The boy with no name?

GRACE shrugs.

Haven't your parents ever told you they love you?

GRACE: Not like that. Not like they mean it. They say it like they're ordering a curry. Love you. Love you.

PETE enters the garden from the side of the stage. He's carrying a large plant. GRACE and LINDA watch as he puts it down, goes to the watering can, waters it. He puts the can down, walks into the lounge.

LINDA: Big plant.

PETE: Left over from a job. They've got more money than brains. That's rich people for you. Unless they give all their money to me, in which case they're really clever. Thought your mother could have this one. Stop her saying I never give her anything.

GRACE: She'll like that.

LINDA: She can take it home with her later.

PETE: Any chance of a drink?

LINDA: You or your plant? (*Beat.*) How was the interview?

PETE: Seemed to go okay. It's hard to tell. I think I sounded horticultural. They said I had the hands of a gardener.

LINDA: Dirty?

PETE: Strong.

LINDA: Beer?

PETE: Yes please.

LINDA: Grace?

GRACE: No thanks.

LINDA exits. PETE unlaces his boots.

PETE: Go on, have a drink.

GRACE: I'm not drinking.

PETE: You alright?

GRACE: Why shouldn't I be?

PETE: No reason.

PETE takes a packet of cigarettes out of his bag.

GRACE: Don't smoke in here.

PETE: Who said I was going to?

He offers one to GRACE. She shakes her head.

No alcohol, no fags. Are you sure you're a teenager?

GRACE: We're not all chain smoking, drug taking piss heads.

PETE lights his cigarette, looking at GRACE all the time.

What you staring at?

PETE: You.

GRACE: Yeah, well mind the wind doesn't change.

LINDA enters with a beer. PETE blows smoke into the air.

LINDA: Can you do that outside?

PETE blows more smoke.

Please.

PETE moves to the back doors, exhales smoke outside.

What's wrong?

GRACE: He's annoying me.

LINDA: He does that sometimes.

PETE: I can hear you.

LINDA: And move your boots. Bloody great things.

PETE puffs on his cigarette, blows smoke into the air.

Pete!

PETE sighs, enters the house, picks up his boots.

PETE: I thought one of the reasons you liked me was
because of my feet.

LINDA: Yeah, your feet, your long smooth toes. Not your
great big dirty boots.

PETE: Is that right?

LINDA: That's right. I love you.

PETE: And I love you.

PETE goes to LINDA and kisses her.

GRACE: Can I do anything?

LINDA: Like what?

GRACE: Ironing.

PETE: Who irons?

GRACE: I do. Can I? I'm good.

LINDA: I'm sure you are.

GRACE: You two have a rest. Take it easy. Put your feet up.

LINDA: I'm fine. Are you alright?

GRACE: (*Laughs nervously.*) Yeah.

> *PETE and LINDA look at GRACE who doesn't move. She just glares at them.*

> I'm pregnant.

LINDA: What?

PETE: What?

GRACE: I'm pregnant.

LINDA: Pregnant?

GRACE: Yes. Sorry Linda.

LINDA: What do you mean, pregnant?

GRACE: I'm having a baby.

LINDA: You can't be.

GRACE: I am.

LINDA: Whose baby?

> *GRACE shrugs.*

> That boy?

PETE: What boy?

LINDA: That boy she's seeing. Is it his?

> *Beat.*

GRACE: Yeah.

LINDA: Have you told him?

GRACE: I might have.

PETE: What does that mean?

LINDA: That she might have.

PETE: She's lying.

GRACE: She's not.

LINDA: Is it his?

GRACE: Yeah. It's his baby. He's the dad.

LINDA: God.

PETE: It takes two to share a bed.

GRACE: Who says we did it in a bed?

LINDA: He should know better. He's older.

PETE: How do you know it's his?

GRACE: I don't sleep around. It happens all the time. To teenagers. One bonk and we're mothers. I didn't do it on purpose.

PETE: She's too young to be a mother.

LINDA: And I'm too old but it doesn't always work out like that.

KATE enters by the back door. PETE stubs out his cigarette. LINDA walks towards KATE.

KATE: You really shouldn't leave that door open.

LINDA: We've been doing it for years.

KATE: It's dangerous.

PETE: Are you sure?

GRACE: Yeah.

PETE: Definitely…?

GRACE: I did a test. Peed on a stick. I missed a period. I had a feeling. You always read about it, women having feelings and you never think it's true. Why should I be any different to anyone else?

LINDA enters with KATE. KATE holds some letters out to GRACE.

KATE: Before I forget.

GRACE glares at the letters. KATE offers the letters to GRACE. GRACE turns away. LINDA goes to her.

What's the matter with her?

PETE shrugs.

Hormones?

PETE: You could say that.

KATE: Is she okay?

PETE: Yeah.

KATE: Only I never know what to expect. I never know whether she'll throw her arms around me or totally ignore me.

PETE: Yeah.

KATE: She likes you a lot.

PETE: Really.

KATE: Respects you.

PETE: Great.

KATE: It's always Pete this and Pete that. She's not being a handful?

GRACE: Mum, I need to talk to you.

KATE: What is it?

GRACE looks at PETE. PETE looks at LINDA.

LINDA: You don't have to do this.

KATE: What's going on?

PETE: Grace…

Pause.

GRACE: I'm pregnant.

KATE: What do you mean pregnant?

PETE: Get a pen and paper and I'll draw you a bloody diagram.

KATE: Oh God.

GRACE: Is that all you can say?

KATE: I knew this would happen.

GRACE: No you didn't.

KATE: Whose is it?

GRACE: Mine.

KATE: I'm not ready to be a grandmother.

PETE: I think we should all calm down.

GRACE: I'm calm.

KATE: How do you know?

PETE: She did a test. She missed a period.

KATE: I've missed several, doesn't mean I'm pregnant.

GRACE: I'm not stupid.

KATE: I never said you were.

GRACE: You talk to me like I am. All the time. Just because I'm sixteen doesn't mean I don't have a brain.

Beat.

KATE: How pregnant?

GRACE: I'm not sure.

KATE: How long have you known?

GRACE: A couple of weeks.

KATE: Why didn't you say something?

GRACE: Nothing to say. I wanted to wait.

KATE: What for?

GRACE: I don't know.

KATE: I want to see evidence.

PETE: You'll have to wait a few months.

KATE: Not that kind of evidence.

GRACE: Alright.

They all stand, not knowing what to do or say.

LINDA: I've got a tester left over. In the bathroom.

GRACE starts to follow LINDA out of the room. KATE follows.

GRACE: I know how to pee on a stick.

KATE stays where she is.

KATE: Don't cheat.

GRACE looks at her mother, incredulous.

GRACE: I'll try not to.

GRACE exits. PETE lights a cigarette. KATE takes it out of his hand, puffs.

PETE: You don't smoke.

KATE: I know. But isn't this what I'm supposed to do?

PETE takes the cigarette away from KATE, stubs it out. LINDA enters.

She can't be pregnant.

PETE: I think she can. I thought she was on the pill?

KATE: I thought he'd use condoms.

PETE: Yeah. Stupid bastard.

PETE walks out to the garden, where he sits on an upturned plant pot and smokes.

KATE: Sorry Linda. This must be really hard for you.

LINDA: Yeah, actually. It is.

KATE: I'm sure she didn't do it on purpose.

LINDA: No one ever does.

PETE turns, talks loudly to KATE from outside.

PETE: I've got something for you Kate.

KATE: Another surprise?

PETE: Ficus Elastica.

KATE exits on to the patio.

KATE: It's huge.

PETE: Left over from a job. It's yours if you want it.

KATE: What did you say it was called again?

PETE: Ficus Elastica.

KATE: Ficus Elastica.

PETE looks at his watch. KATE paces, LINDA sits down. GRACE enters with the stick in her hand. She looks at LINDA. PETE and KATE enter the living room.

That was quick.

GRACE: I was peeing on a piece of plastic, not having open heart surgery.

KATE: Let me see.

GRACE looks at the stick, looks at LINDA.

She's making it up.

GRACE: She is not making it up.

GRACE holds out the stick to KATE.

Pause.

KATE: Whose is it?

GRACE: (*Meaning LINDA.*) Well it's not hers.

KATE: I mean whose baby is it? Is it that boy's?

GRACE: Might be.

KATE: Tell me.

GRACE: No.

KATE: Then maybe you'll tell your father.

GRACE: It's none of your business.

KATE: I think it is.

GRACE: Piss off. Piss right off.

KATE slaps GRACE across the face. Both of them are shocked.

Feel better now you've slapped a pregnant woman?

KATE: You're not a pregnant woman. You're a pregnant child.

LINDA: Go home Kate. Come back in the morning.

KATE: And do what? This has to be resolved.

LINDA: There's nothing to resolve. She's pregnant.

KATE: Does she want it?

LINDA: We haven't got that far.

KATE: Who's we? She's my child.

LINDA: And right now you're the last person she needs to be with.

KATE: I don't understand.

LINDA: She's in shock.

KATE: So am I.

LINDA: Kate, come on. Be more sensitive.

KATE: Grace…

GRACE can't look at her mother.

What did I do wrong?

PETE: Nothing Kate. You did nothing wrong.

KATE: Then why won't she talk to me? This is my grandchild we're talking about. Grace?

Pause.

LINDA: Grace?

GRACE shrugs, she's crying.

Go home, Kate.

KATE: What do I tell Mike?

LINDA: Nothing. Absolutely nothing. Not yet.

KATE: Grace… I care about you. You do know that?

KATE tries to hug GRACE. GRACE turns away from KATE. KATE exits, PETE follows her out.

GRACE: She doesn't understand. She doesn't get it. She thinks I'm doing it for attention.

LINDA: And are you?

GRACE: How can you say that?

GRACE wipes a tear from her eye.

This wasn't supposed to happen. It wasn't planned.

LINDA: It never is.

GRACE: And before… What I said, it was out of order.

LINDA: No it wasn't. (*Beat.*) It was cruel.

Pause.

GRACE: I'm sorry.

LINDA: How do you feel?

GRACE: Shocked. Scared.

LINDA: Do you feel sick?

GRACE: No. Did you?

LINDA: Once.

GRACE: Are you angry with me?

LINDA: Yes.

GRACE: Yeah.

LINDA: Does he know? He should know.

GRACE: I don't want to tell him. There's no point. I mean, there's no point, is there?

GRACE starts to cry. It is controlled, calm. LINDA walks up to GRACE, holds her, comforts her. Lights fade.

Scene 7

Later that night. It's totally dark except for a dim outside light. PETE is looking at the stars. GRACE walks into the lounge. She watches PETE. He burps loudly. She laughs. He turns round, smiles at her. She walks out to the garden.

GRACE: Star gazing?

PETE: Yeah, that one's Brad Pitt, that's the Julia Roberts constellation, and that one is really special.

GRACE: Oh yeah?

PETE: That star belongs to Linda.

GRACE: You bought a star for Linda?

PETE: Yeah. For her fortieth.

GRACE: How amazing.

PETE: I thought so.

GRACE: Why didn't I know about it?

PETE: You probably weren't interested.

Pause.

GRACE: I like it out here.

PETE: Yeah. It's good. But I wish it was mine. It's not the same when it belongs to someone else. It's temporary.

GRACE: Isn't everything?

PETE: You're not stupid are you?

GRACE: No.

PETE: You okay?

GRACE: Yeah. You?

Beat.

PETE: Linda asleep?

GRACE: Must be. Unless she's gone for a midnight walk with her secret lover. It's a joke.

PETE: I wouldn't blame her.

GRACE: Pete!

PETE: I mean, she's supported me more than anyone, with my new business. She's worked extra hours at school, talked about taking a promotion which I know she doesn't want to do, but she would, and what does she get in return?

GRACE: A man who loves her.

PETE: Can you tell?

GRACE: Yeah. Are you annoyed with me?

Beat.

PETE: Yes.

GRACE: It was an accident Pete.

PETE: I know.

GRACE: Condom burst.

PETE: I don't need to know the details.

GRACE: It's amazing. All those little blokes swimming their way up inside you on the exact day you drop an egg. I mean the chances of that happening... I am careful you know.

PETE: Yeah.

GRACE: I am. I don't have sex with everyone I meet.

PETE: You wanted to have sex with me.

GRACE: I was joking.

PETE: Thanks very much. What would you have done if I'd said yes?

GRACE shrugs.

GRACE: I can't help it if I find you attractive.

PETE: It must be hard.

GRACE: I don't know what to do Pete.

PETE: What about?

GRACE: The baby.

PETE: Do you want it?

GRACE: Do I want it?

PETE: Yeah, do you want it? Do you want a baby? Do you want to be a parent, have responsibilities, not have a life of your own?

GRACE: Not when you put it like that.

PETE: What were you thinking? Romantic walks in the park with a baby strapped to the front of your body? As much sleep as you get now, all the time in the world, you won't be able to do things the same way you know. It'll be different.

GRACE: Is that really what you want?

PETE: Yes. More than anything. I want to stay awake, to drive him around in the car so he'll go to sleep. I want to stay in instead of going out to dinner with people who bore me.

GRACE: You make it sound like a child is your way of escaping from your life.

PETE: Well maybe that's what I want. To escape. To do it differently. To have someone to do it differently with.

GRACE: You've got Linda.

PETE: I want a child. And I can't have one. Has she said anything?

GRACE: No.

PETE: She wants you to keep it?

GRACE: She doesn't.

PETE: She wants you to get rid of it?

GRACE: No.

PETE: What do you think you'll do?

GRACE: Sit out here with you.

PETE: Shouldn't you be studying?

GRACE: I'm bored with studying.

PETE: It's important.

GRACE: I know. But I like it out here.

PETE: So do I. (*Beat.*) Why do you hate your mum so much?

GRACE: I don't hate her.

PETE: Then why are you so nasty to her?

GRACE: She's nasty to me.

PETE: She loves you.

GRACE: Yeah.

PETE: Are you ashamed of her?

GRACE: No.

PETE: Then what is it with you?

GRACE: She's boring.

PETE: She's your mother, she's not supposed to be everything you want her to be.

GRACE: I don't want her to be anything.

PETE: Am I boring?

GRACE: No. You and Linda, you're great. Really interesting.

PETE: Your mother is too. You just don't give her a chance.

GRACE: How do I do that?

PETE: Hear what she has to say.

GRACE: I do.

PETE: You don't. You listen, but you don't hear.

GRACE: What are you, some kind of therapist? (*Beat.*) Will you teach me how to be a gardener?

PETE: What do you mean?

GRACE: Give me lessons. About plants and things.

PETE: Plants and things. Yeah, if you like.

GRACE: I'm sorry Pete.

PETE: Yeah.

GRACE: Do you want anything?

PETE shakes his head.

See you in the morning then.

PETE: Yeah.

GRACE: Night night.

PETE: Don't let the bed bugs bite.

GRACE: I think they already have.

GRACE exits. PETE leans back, looks up at the stars. Lights fade.

Scene 8

The following morning. The TV is on. The volume hardly audible. The lights come up slowly. GRACE sits on the floor, knees bent into her. LINDA enters with a mug of tea, which she hands to GRACE. GRACE sips, winces.

GRACE: No sugar?

LINDA: If you're going to keep that baby, sugar's out.

GRACE: I didn't say I was.

LINDA: You didn't say you weren't. Your mum will be here soon.

GRACE: She'll be late.

LINDA: Aren't you going to get dressed?

GRACE: I am dressed.

LINDA: What's the problem?

GRACE: No problem. Apart from the fact that I'm pregnant. (*Beat.*) I know this is a stupid question, but I'll ask it anyway.

LINDA: Go ahead.

GRACE: What…what…would you do if you were me? Only if I ask mum she'll say that means I want to keep it, but…what would you do?

LINDA takes a moment. GRACE thinks she has offended LINDA. GRACE is filled with anticipation.

LINDA: I had an abortion.

Beat.

GRACE: When you were my age?

LINDA shakes her head.

LINDA: Thirty-one.

GRACE: What about Pete?

Beat.

LINDA: It wasn't Pete's.

Pause.

It was just after I'd met him. We weren't really in a relationship. We were going out, to the cinema, having dinner.

GRACE: Having sex?

LINDA: Yeah.

GRACE: So how can you be sure it wasn't Pete's?

LINDA: I know it wasn't his.

GRACE: Whose then? (*Beat.*) Affair?

LINDA: It just happened. He was there. Looking at me like I mattered. Like I was this fantastic special woman. And at the time, while it was happening, it seemed perfectly okay, perfectly right. I thought I could deal with it, you know, a few discreet evenings that meant nothing more than sex.

GRACE: Why haven't you told Pete?

LINDA: There's no point. Not now. I thought I could cope. With him. With the pregnancy.

GRACE: But you couldn't?

LINDA: Maybe that was my only chance. To have a kid. And I screwed up.

GRACE: And now you feel guilty?

LINDA: Not guilty. Never guilty. Just sad.

GRACE: Why are you telling me this?

LINDA: To try and help you make sense of it.

GRACE: Does mum know?

LINDA: No one knows.

GRACE: Why me?

LINDA: Because you're here. Because the words came out before I could stop them.

GRACE: You're not trying to make me have it?

LINDA: Just think about what you're doing.

GRACE: I don't want a lecture on how terrible abortion is.

LINDA: I don't think it's terrible. I did it didn't I? All I'm saying is think about what you're doing.

Pause.

GRACE: Who was he?

LINDA: A supply teacher. He was twenty-five, enthusiastic. Actually, he was quite a lot like Pete. A younger version of Pete. Maybe that's why I found him so attractive. He didn't mean anything to me. It was just…

GRACE: Sex?

LINDA: Yeah.

GRACE: Why didn't you keep it? If you wanted a child so much why didn't you keep it?

LINDA: I didn't want one then. Neither of us did. How could we? We were at the beginning of something new. We hardly knew each other. Our relationship was exciting, fresh, the last thing Pete and I wanted was a kid. We thought we had all the time in the world. We were young, we wanted to have fun. Kids were for later, when we were tired of each other and ran out of surprises.

GRACE: Would you have kept it, if you'd known what was going to happen?

LINDA: I didn't know what was going to happen. I knew the sun would rise and the moon would set, I knew my parents would die and my hair would turn grey. But I didn't know I'd never be able to have another child. To keep another child inside me like that one.

GRACE: Were you very pregnant?

LINDA: Eleven weeks.

GRACE: Why did you wait so long?

LINDA: Why are you waiting?

GRACE: Didn't Pete guess?

LINDA: Pete's not very good at guessing. All I'm saying is, there are some things that are definite, that we know will happen, and others that surprise us. When you're younger and you have time, nothing seems urgent, everything seems possible. A month goes by and then a year, then two. And then you're forty and your body starts to change. And then you're forty-one and forty-two and fifty is only eight years away. Outside you have a few wrinkles, but inside, that's where it's all really going on. But because you can't see it you forget, you believe it isn't really happening. Not to you. To everyone else, but not to you. Because you're special. You're different. You're the one who'll prove science wrong. But I'm not different.

GRACE: Can't you tell Pete?

LINDA: Never. I can never tell him.

PETE enters.

PETE: What can't you tell me?

LINDA: That I love you.

PETE: You just told me.

LINDA: Must be stupid then.

PETE: Must be.

GRACE gives LINDA a hug and kiss. As LINDA exits –

Make mine a black coffee please.

LINDA: Make it yourself.

LINDA exits.

PETE: Sleep alright?

GRACE: Yeah.

The doorbell rings.

LINDA: (*Off.*) One of you get that.

The doorbell rings again.

Pete! Grace!

GRACE unwillingly moves her body off the sofa, goes to the hall, presses the buzzer and returns to the sofa. A moment later KATE appears. KATE looks tired. She stands on the threshold.

PETE: Morning.

KATE: Morning.

PETE: Sleep okay?

KATE: Like a baby.

PETE: Grace, cup of tea…

GRACE: I've got one thanks.

PETE: …for your mum.

GRACE: Please.

PETE: Please.

GRACE: Okay. (*To KATE.*) You look like you've been to a funeral.

PETE raises his eyebrows at GRACE. GRACE moves to the door.

KATE: Actually, I'd prefer coffee.

KATE/GRACE: (*Together.*) White, two sugars.

KATE: Thanks.

As GRACE exits LINDA enters.

LINDA: How are you this morning?

KATE: Sparkly and enthusiastic and looking forward to the day ahead. Has she said anything?

LINDA: No.

KATE: What are we going to do?

LINDA: It's up to her.

KATE: What if she wants to keep it?

LINDA: Then she'll keep it.

KATE: And what if she doesn't want it?

PETE: Then she won't. There aren't that many choices.

KATE: I want her to keep it.

LINDA: What?

KATE: I think it might be the right thing to do.

PETE: Who for?

KATE: I hope you haven't been encouraging her to get rid of it?

LINDA: This is her decision.

Pause.

KATE: I didn't want her.

LINDA: What do you mean?

KATE: When I was pregnant. I didn't want a baby. She wasn't planned. I was in a great job, about to be promoted. Mike kept going on and on about babies and shouldn't we start a family. I made a pact with myself. I said I'd come off all contraception for six months. I didn't tell Mike. He was stressed enough. And if nothing had happened after six months…well, I didn't really think it through. But then I didn't need to. Grace came along, surprised us. Surprised me. I almost didn't go through with it.

LINDA: I don't understand.

KATE : I almost didn't go through with it.

LINDA: How can you tell me that?

KATE: I need you to know how I felt. How I feel. While I was pregnant, all that time, I didn't want her. Even after she was born, it took a while to like her. To look at that round face, those big eyes, and accept that this was it. And then I fell in love with her. Like never before. I loved her more than I loved Mike, more than the boys. More than anyone. (*Beat.*) I want her to keep it.

LINDA: So she can be like you?

KATE: No.

LINDA: So she can be just like you?

GRACE enters with coffee –

KATE: Look, I'm sorry, yesterday, I didn't mean to…

GRACE: It doesn't matter.

KATE: How are you?

GRACE shrugs.

GRACE: Sore breasts.

Pause.

KATE: Your room's ready.

GRACE: Ready?

KATE: If you want to come home. The boys helped me paint it. Purple. You said you always wanted a purple bedroom.

GRACE: I hate purple.

KATE: Shall I just go?

GRACE: Yeah. (*Beat.*) No. Stay. I want you to stay. Did you tell dad?

KATE shakes her head.

LINDA: We need to talk.

GRACE: Okay.

KATE: Whatever you want to do will be fine with me.

PETE: We'll help in any way we can.

GRACE: Have you lot been discussing this?

LINDA: No.

KATE: She might want to keep it. Do you want to keep it?

GRACE: No.

KATE: You want to get rid of it?

GRACE: No.

KATE: Then what?

Pause.

GRACE: I want to give it to you.

KATE: Me?

GRACE: To Linda.

LINDA: Don't be ridiculous. You can't just give me your baby.

GRACE: You want one don't you?

LINDA: Not like this.

KATE: It's not the done thing.

GRACE: And what is the done thing? Give birth to it and give it to some complete stranger, who might love it, if I'm lucky.

LINDA: It's very sweet of you, but this isn't about me, it's about you.

KATE: Grace, you're being very childish.

GRACE: I am a child. But I've thought about it. Really, I have. I know you probably think it's too soon, and that I'll change my mind, but I want you to have it.

KATE: Is that why you did this, as some sort of heroic gesture?

GRACE: I didn't plan it.

KATE: You're insane.

GRACE: You asked me what I wanted and I'm telling you.

KATE: You don't know what you want.

GRACE: How do you know?

KATE: Because you need time to think. When you feel it inside you, growing, pushing, being part of you, you'll feel differently about it. Either keep it or get rid of it.

PETE: She can't get rid of it.

GRACE: You said you'd support me in whatever I did.

PETE: I didn't think you'd want to get rid of it. Linda, tell her, she can't get rid of it.

Beat.

Linda, tell her.

GRACE: They want a baby, I don't. I'm having one, they're not. I'm offering them the chance to have what they've always wanted. What they'll never have again. It's not that complicated.

PETE: It's not a bloody competition. The first five callers have won our star prize. It's a child.

GRACE: This isn't all my fault.

KATE: Tell us who he is. He should know, be aware of what he's done. He should be responsible.

GRACE: And what will you do? Tell him off, smack his bottom, yell and say he's been a very bad boy.

GRACE exits. KATE moves to follow GRACE.

LINDA: Leave her.

Pause.

PETE: Euro for them.

LINDA: What?

PETE: Euro for them. You know, was penny, now Euro. What's going on in that head?

LINDA: You don't want to know.

PETE: I do.

LINDA: Really, you don't.

PETE: She wants to give us her baby.

LINDA: Yeah.

PETE: Insane.

LINDA: Like something out of a fairy story.

PETE: We'll have a happy ending then.

(*To KATE.*) Alright?

KATE: No.

PETE: No.

KATE: She really wants you to have it.

PETE: Yeah.

KATE: Like it's some kind of gift from God.

PETE: Course it is. But it's her gift, not ours.

KATE: This isn't funny Pete.

PETE: I'm not laughing, Kate.

KATE: She should never have come to stay with you.

LINDA: Hold on.

PETE: It's not our fault.

KATE: Filling her head with baby talk.

PETE: We haven't filled her head with anything. This has nothing to do with me and Linda.

KATE: She hears you, talking about babies, about your problems, and she wants to help.

LINDA: She came here to get away from you.

KATE: I'm her mother.

LINDA: Doesn't mean she has to like you.

Pause.

KATE: You can't have it.

PETE: Who says we will.

KATE: It's not right. You can't do it.

LINDA: You're jealous.

KATE: Of what?

LINDA: My relationship with Grace.

PETE: Linda!

KATE: Not at all.

LINDA: You are.

KATE: It's my grandchild. How can you even think about adopting it?

PETE: We wouldn't be able to adopt it.

KATE: Do you know everything Pete?

PETE: Actually yes I do.

PETE exits.

KATE: She thinks you can. She thinks she'll give you her baby and everyone will have what they want and we'll be happy families.

LINDA: And what do you want?

KATE: I want my daughter back.

LINDA: She never went away.

Pause.

KATE: It's too soon to make a decision. She needs time to be with it, with the idea of being pregnant.

LINDA: It's not an idea, it's happening.

KATE: I can look after it, while she goes to school and university.

LINDA: Is that what you really want at your age? A small baby?

KATE: It's what you and Pete want.

LINDA: It's not the same.

KATE: It is. If she gave it to you, would you take it?

LINDA: I can't answer that.

KATE: Linda?

LINDA: I don't know.

KATE: You would, wouldn't you?

LINDA: What do you think?

KATE: I think you would.

LINDA laughs with disbelief.

LINDA: Yeah, of course you do.

KATE: I didn't mean…

LINDA: Yeah you did.

Lights down.

Scene 9

Afternoon. GRACE sits outside on an upturned plant pot. LINDA stands by the sofa. GRACE gets up, turns around, sees LINDA.

GRACE: How long have you been watching me?

Beat.

LINDA: Since about two hours after you were born.

GRACE: That long?

LINDA: Yeah.

Beat.

GRACE: What was it like, seeing me as a baby?

LINDA: I burst into tears the first time I saw you.

GRACE: Because I was so ugly?

LINDA: Because I couldn't believe how small you were. And because you'd come out of my sister's body.

GRACE: Did she love me?

LINDA: Your mum? Yeah. Course.

GRACE: But she never wanted me?

LINDA: She didn't plan you, which isn't the same thing.

GRACE: But you make plans for things you want.

LINDA: And sometimes you get surprised. You get something else, something you thought you might not want or like or need. She got you. How fortunate is that. (*Beat.*) I heard this story, about new-born babies. Apparently, they know everything. They have total knowledge. And when they're born, this dip (*Pointing to the dip above her top lip.*) is filled out. The moment they're born, an angel puts his finger on that spot and a dip appears…and suddenly all their knowledge is gone…and they have to learn all over again.

GRACE: Is that true?

LINDA: If you want it to be.

Beat.

GRACE: I'm not ready to be a parent.

LINDA: I'm not ready to be anything. No one ever is.

GRACE: Really?

LINDA: We always planned to have a baby, not to not have one. We planned for the spare room to be the baby's room, not my office. Those walls were meant to be a different shade. There should have been a cot and a musical mobile and the smell should have been sweet, not musty from old books.

Beat.

GRACE: His name's Ryan. He's eighteen. He's a mechanic. He doesn't love me.

LINDA: Did he say?

GRACE: He said, I don't love you.

LINDA: Do you love him?

GRACE: Don't know. Don't think so. Isn't it meant to hurt down here (*Pointing to below her stomach.*) when you're in love?

LINDA: At first. Then it just becomes more of a dull ache. I thought you said he loved you? Before, you said someone said they loved you. Wasn't it him?

GRACE shakes her head.

GRACE: I can't imagine it.

LINDA: What?

GRACE: Having a baby. Giving birth to a shrivelled up piece of me and some bloke I don't even like, who smells of diesel and tobacco and thinks a Thatcherite is someone who fixes roofs.

Beat.

LINDA: You don't want it?

GRACE: I do. (*Beat.*) Just not now.

LINDA: Then when?

GRACE: When it's right.

LINDA: It might never be right.

GRACE: When I meet someone I love. Really love. Who loves me.

LINDA: What if you don't?

GRACE: I will. Everyone meets at least one person in a lifetime.

LINDA: That's it then?

GRACE: Yeah. That's it. I'm making an appointment.

LINDA: Where?

GRACE: At a Clinic.

LINDA: Grace.

GRACE: I don't want it. You don't want it.

LINDA: I didn't say that.

GRACE: Do you want it?

LINDA: No.

GRACE: See.

LINDA: It's different.

GRACE: It's a baby isn't it?

LINDA: It's your baby.

GRACE: What's wrong with my baby?

LINDA: It's yours.

GRACE: Then tell me to keep it. Tell me that getting rid of it is the wrong thing to do.

LINDA: I can't.

GRACE: Go on. Go on Linda. Tell me.

GRACE exits. LINDA's eyes glisten and fill with tears.

PETE enters from the side of the garden with a bottle of champagne. LINDA wipes her eyes, exits to the garden.

PETE: Who's a clever man then.

LINDA: You?

PETE: Is the right answer.

LINDA: You got the job?

PETE: I got the job. They said I could chose my hours. They've got a staff canteen, a gym, crèche. Parking. And I get paid holiday.

PETE goes to a cupboard, takes out two pint glasses. He looks at LINDA.

Aren't you going to congratulate me?

LINDA: Congratulations.

PETE dips his hand into his jacket pocket, removes a small green velvet box.

What's that?

PETE: Looks like a small green velvet box to me. Don't just stare at it.

LINDA opens the box, removes a small diamond ring.

LINDA: What's this for?

PETE takes her hand.

PETE: I love you. I want to marry you.

LINDA: You're proposing?

PETE: Yes.

LINDA: Aren't you going to get down on one knee?

PETE: I was about to.

PETE lowers himself onto one knee. He notices LINDA has been crying.

What's wrong?

LINDA shrugs.

Is it the baby? Is it because you want it? Because I do Linda. I've been thinking about it, all day. And I think it could work. Really work. I'd work harder, longer hours so you could give up your job, stay at home. Or I could stay at home. I don't mind being a house husband. House partner. We'd have everything we've always wanted. It could work.

LINDA cries harder.

PETE: What's happened?

LINDA: Grace. She doesn't want it.

PETE: The baby?

LINDA: She doesn't want it.

PETE: You should have told her Linda, stopped her.

LINDA: It's not my decision.

PETE: You can't let her do it. Not after what we've been through.

LINDA: It's up to her.

PETE: It's a child. It's special.

LINDA: I can't make her do anything.

PETE: We haven't talked about it. You and me.

LINDA: We're talking about it now. (*Beat.*) I was beginning to make plans. In my head. Moving forwards.

PETE: But we could have what we've always wanted.

LINDA: I don't think Grace giving us her baby, like it's some special present we deserve, is having what we've always wanted.

PETE: You're selfish.

LINDA: That's not what I'd call myself.

PETE: What would you call yourself then?

LINDA: Try realistic. Honest.

PETE: And what would you call a woman who doesn't know when her partner is so fucking sad that he might just be hurting more than he's ever hurt. More than he hurt when his gran died, more than he hurt when he fell off his bike and cut his knee open. More than anyone ever hurt in the whole world. What would you call that?

LINDA: I don't know.

PETE: You don't know because there isn't a word. It hasn't been invented yet. (*Beat.*) Did you tell her to get rid of it?

LINDA: No.

PETE: You didn't tell her not to?

LINDA: It's her baby.

PETE: It could be ours.

LINDA: I don't want to have this conversation now.

PETE: Then when? In a year, in six months time, when
you've got over never having children…

LINDA: I'll never get over it.

PETE: …When I'm only just beginning to come to terms
with it. Tell me when you're ready to talk about it and
I'll put it in my diary. (*Beat.*) Is it because my body
works?

LINDA: Stop it.

PETE: Because mine can still make it work? Well you know
what, I might just go off and have sex with some
underage girl with an angel's face and Malibu breath. I
might just do it.

LINDA: Shut up.

PETE: Just because you've decided that you don't want
Grace's baby doesn't mean I have to agree with it.

LINDA: How can I take Grace's baby? I look at her, and I
see a young woman, with so much excitement ahead of
her. And I have to remember that I had that excitement
too. I had everything she has. Only I did it differently.
And now I have a different excitement. When I was
twelve, my mother learned how to drive. I remember the
day she went for her driving test. This old bloke with
greying hair came to pick her up. I thought he was old.
He was probably as old as I am now. Dad had taken her
for a lesson in the morning, they'd had their usual
argument about how she parked too close to the curb.
She said she didn't. He showed her where the tyres were

scuffed from the dust. She came home, smiling and waving. And I knew she'd achieved something fantastic. She'd found a new independence. Apart from dad, apart from us, apart from the rest of her life.

PETE: I don't understand.

LINDA: She was in control. I haven't been in control of my life for years. Everyone else has. I want to be in control again Pete. I was just getting used to being us again.

PETE: We've always been us.

LINDA: No talk of babies, injections, hospital visits. I was just getting used to it Pete.

Pause.

Do you honestly think I could take a child from her? With Kate and Mike and everyone else glaring at me as if I'm some crazed woman who has finally got what she's wanted. Well you know what, I don't think I'm that woman anymore, and I don't think it's what I want. Not like this. I wanted our baby, yours and mine. I wanted to be pregnant and feel it kicking, and be all those things I'm never going to be. But if I can't be that woman, I'll settle for the one I've always been. Because actually, I quite like her. She's funny, amusing, intelligent, can look quite pretty if she tries. What do you want more Pete? Me or a baby?

PETE exits.

LINDA goes to the cabinet, takes the video out of the drawer, pulls out the tape, slowly at first then faster and more furiously until it resembles unravelled wool. Lights fade.

Scene 10

GRACE sits on the sofa, her back-pack is on the ground beside her. KATE is standing at the door, car keys in hand.

KATE: All ready then?

GRACE: Yeah.

KATE: You're sure this is what you want?

GRACE: Yeah.

KATE: Because if you want to change your mind, that's fine with me.

GRACE: I don't want to.

KATE: Have you said goodbye to Linda and Pete?

GRACE: Not yet.

KATE: Don't you want to? (*Beat.*) You could leave them a note?

GRACE: Maybe.

KATE: Come on then.

As GRACE gets up, LINDA enters. She is surprised to see KATE.

We were just talking about you.

LINDA: Oh yeah.

KATE: We're off now.

LINDA: Already?

KATE: No point delaying it is there?

LINDA: Suppose not.

GRACE: I'll wait in the car Mum.

KATE: I won't be long.

LINDA tries to hug GRACE. GRACE pulls away. She goes to KATE, KATE gives her the car keys.

I love you Grace.

GRACE smiles at KATE, and exits.

Thanks.

LINDA: That's alright.

KATE: She's going off to France, with friends. Did she tell you?

LINDA shakes her head.

I thought it would be good. Help her…you know…get over it. Although Mike thinks she should get a job. Work her way through the summer.

LINDA: Yeah.

KATE: We got summer jobs, washed people's cars.

LINDA: You never washed anyone's car.

KATE: I did. Remember Mr Toilet?

LINDA: Mr Toilet?

KATE: Lived at number fifty-six. The house with the hedge that looked like a cat. He had that old green station wagon. I can still remember the registration. BOG 125C.

LINDA: Mr Toilet!

KATE: It had wood panelling and all that bloody chrome. God, I hated polishing it.

LINDA: You cleaned Mr Toilet's car?

KATE: Once. Never again. (*Beat.*) Come for dinner.

LINDA: Okay.

KATE: I mean it. I haven't cooked for you in ages. You and Pete. Next week.

LINDA: Yeah, great.

KATE: Grace will be gone, the boys are staying with friends in Devon. It'll be just the four of us. Like before, before the kids. Like we used to be with mum and dad, the four of us, before I met Mike and you met Pete. (*Beat.*) Better go. (*Beat.*) You know, you are special Linda. Really special.

KATE kisses LINDA, holds her. KATE exits.

LINDA stands for a moment, totally still. She walks outside, sits on the upturned plant pot. PETE enters the garden from the side door, carrying a small plant.

LINDA: Did you see them?

PETE: Yeah, just now. (*Beat.*) Are they…?

LINDA: Yeah.

Beat.

Another plant?

PETE: This one's special. (*Beat.*) It's for the baby.

LINDA: Grace's baby?

PETE: Our baby. Babies. All of them. It's sort of a symbol of something new. Of us moving on.

PETE gets on his knees, tips the plant upside down, makes space in a patch of earth.

Help me.

LINDA: What is it?

PETE: Gypsophila Paniculata. Baby's breath.

PETE puts it into the ground. He takes some compost, scatters a hand full around the base of the plant.

Say something.

LINDA: Like what?

PETE: I don't know, something relevant.

LINDA: About the babies?

PETE: No, about the moon.

LINDA: Thank you for coming, even though it was briefly. We don't know why you didn't stay, but hopefully you've found other homes. We loved you. (*Beat.*) We love you.

PETE: I love you.

PETE kisses LINDA on the cheek. PETE fills the can, waters the plant.

LINDA: That's good. Because I love you too.

PETE: You hungry?

LINDA: Starving.

PETE: You don't know the meaning of starving.

LINDA: I fancy a big juicy steak.

PETE: With chips.

LINDA: Baked potato.

PETE: Mayonnaise.

LINDA: Ketchup.

PETE: You and me.

LINDA: You and me.

PETE does 'stones paper scissors.' He clenches his fist and punches it into the air three times. When he opens it, his fingers are together, tips pointing upwards and soaring into the sky.

What's that meant to be?

PETE: A lamb chop.

LINDA: It's not.

PETE: Come on then. Come and find out.

LINDA: Where?

PETE: Anywhere you like.

LINDA: What do you mean?

PETE: We're going.

LINDA: Going where?

PETE shrugs, removes two passports from his pocket.

Passports?

PETE: Yeah. We're going somewhere. Anywhere. You and me. Now.

LINDA: We can't.

PETE: We can. We can do anything we want.

LINDA: A cruise on the Nile? You could wear floaty white cotton.

PETE: I've always wanted to imitate bed linen.

LINDA: We can't.

PETE: We can.

LINDA: What about the flat?

PETE: What about it?

LINDA: Your plants? They'll die.

PETE: We'll leave a note for upstairs.

LINDA: School?

PETE: It's the holidays.

LINDA: We'll need visas.

PETE: We'll get them.

LINDA: Injections.

PETE: No more injections.

LINDA: Pete!

PETE: Linda.

LINDA: You're being serious.

PETE: I've never been so serious.

Beat.

LINDA: Alright.

PETE: Alright.

LINDA: I'll need some underwear.

PETE: We'll buy it there.

LINDA: Where?

PETE: Don't know.

LINDA: And my toothbrush.

PETE: Get it at the airport.

LINDA: Which airport?

PETE: Don't know.

LINDA: We can't afford it.

PETE: We'll live off coconuts and make love for two weeks.

LINDA: What about your work?

PETE: It's sorted.

PETE locks the back doors. Lights start to fade.

LINDA: Are you sure?

PETE: Are you?

LINDA: Don't know.

PETE: I know I love you.

LINDA: I know I love you.

PETE: Right then.

LINDA: Right then.

PETE: Shall we go?

LINDA and PETE look around at the flat. They close the door, and for a moment the stage is bare. Blackout.

The End.